Best Practice Guide
for Customer Service Managers

An activity-based workbook for leaders of
teams that strive for service excellence

Trevor Arden & Stephanie Edwards

Customer 1st International Ltd
United Kingdom

Best Practice Guide for Customer Service Managers

Published by Customer 1st International Ltd 2009

ISBN-13: 978-0-9548744-2-1
ISBN-10: 0-9548744-2-0

First published in the UK 2009 by

Customer 1st International Ltd
Bramblewood House
Longbridge Deverill
Wiltshire BA12 7DS
United Kingdom

Printed and bound in the UK by

Solent Design Studio
Claylands Road
Bishops Waltham
Southampton
Hampshire SO32 1BH
United Kingdom

Illustrations by Anne-Marie Sonneveld

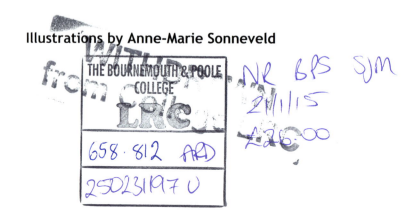

Contents

Introduction

1 Managers and Customer Service Excellence

2 Setting and Communicating Objectives

3 Putting the Customer First

8 Embedding Innovation in Your Team

9 Continuous Professional Development

0   Introduction

Welcome to the Best Practice Guide for Customer Service Managers. It is available in several formats, including e-book and e-workbook. The e-workbook version enables readers to enter their responses to activities and knowledge-checks into Activity Forms, which can then be saved electronically. The completed Activity Forms can be retained as reference documents for work-based improvements, and may also be used to build an e-portfolio, demonstrating the Manager's or Team Leader's achievement of the learning outcomes.

The Best Practice Guide also forms the basis of a tutor-led, online course delivered by Customer 1st International (the publisher of the Best Practice Guide), leading to an Accredited Award. For further information on this course, go to www.customer1st.co.uk.

0.1   Who is this Best Practice Guide For?

The Best Practice Guide for Customer Service Managers is an activity-based improvement programme for Managers and Team Leaders who wish to manage customer service effectively and proactively – through motivating and inspiring their teams. It focuses on meeting and exceeding customer expectations by placing customers at the heart of all the team does.

Exceeding customers' expectations

6

Managers and Team Leaders can make or break an organisation's values. A leader who successfully creates a customer focused culture will have a huge impact on business success - through employee retention and customer loyalty. As a Manager or Team Leader you should communicate your organisation's customer service strategy to your team - to inspire them to exceed their customers' expectations. You can only achieve this if you believe in your own abilities as a manager - leading by example and sharing your positive emotions with your team.

This programme will help you as a Manager or Team Leader to involve your team in decision making, planning and improving. Move beyond the traditional management style - where staff are only given responsibility for the day-to-day tasks and rarely empowered to take the initiative. For World Class Service Excellence, teams need to be fully involved in order to motivate and develop them as customer service professionals. This programme shows you how to keep your team engaged every step of the way.

0.2　How to Use this Best Practice Guide

This Best Practice Guide covers all the knowledge and skills you need as a Manager or Team Leader to deliver excellent customer service. It has been based on the UK's National Occupational Standards for Customer Service. The Guide delivers all the concepts, knowledge and understanding through simple explanations and examples. It then enables you to improve your Management or Team Leading skills by carrying out relevant, work-based activities involving your own team members and customers.

Case Study Organisations

Three case study organisations provide best practice examples to help you to apply the knowledge and understanding presented in the text to real-world situations.

Euro-Deporte

Euro-Deporte became a Europe-wide leisure company in 2007, providing leisure and recreation services across many of the countries of western Europe. Previously owned by a Spanish family, it is now a global player in the leisure industry, with plans to expand further throughout Europe and also into South America. Its organisational strategy has been built around the need to compete through differentiation from its better-resourced competitors. To do this, Euro-Deporte introduced the concept of high-quality customer service.

Unicentro

Originally formed from a chain of retail outlets in Italy, Unicentro has successfully grown its business into a global organisation that develops, owns and manages retail and entertainment centres at hundreds of locations in developed countries across the United States, Europe, Australia and Asia.

The company is widely recognised for its innovative approach to centre management, and its attention to detail in providing a complete solution for retailers. Unicentro delivers solutions for security, customer services, tourist/visitor information and environmental requirements all within its own centre management package. It is currently a popular choice for global retailers wishing to expand their offerings, especially in countries with well-developed retail markets. In addition it focuses as a Business-to-Business (B2B) organisation on helping the smaller retailer to develop their business, through a range of relatively low cost arrangements encouraging new entrants to the retail centre market.

Since it is a B2B company, Unicentro places great importance on managing its customers' experiences. Every retailer that it does business with is allocated to a regional Customer Relationship Manager, who delivers a well developed set of customer relationship management processes and performance management package.

GCU Finance

GCU is a financial services company that offers personal and corporate banking to customers across Europe, Africa and Asia. Formed from a South African online bank's acquisition of a European finance house in 2001, it has been successful in providing a customer focused set of financial services.

The bank has its global headquarters in Johannesburg, with regional centres in Amsterdam, Paris, Lagos, Tokyo and St Petersburg.

From Learning to Action

The Best Practice Guide for Customer Service Managers will help you to track your own progress and improvements. Each module includes an opportunity to update your Team Balanced Scorecard, together with a Team Action Plan and Progress Record. These activities are designed to focus you on making any changes needed straight away, so that your learning results in concrete improvements in your team – driving your organisation towards world class service excellence.

Confirming Your Learning

All of the nine modules include a multi-choice Knowledge-Check consisting of five questions. Each Knowledge-Check allows you to test the progress you have made with your learning programme. You should carry out the self assessment once you have finished going through the module, including all the activities. You will find the answers to the self assessments towards the end of this Best Practice Guide.

0.3 Aims

The aims of the Best Practice Guide for Customer Service Managers are to:

- Introduce participants/readers to the basic principles of managing customer service
- Prepare participants/readers for team leading and management in their sector
- Enable participants/readers to plan and implement an effective service management programme designed to deliver customer service excellence

0.4 Learning Outcomes

The Learning Outcomes for each module are shown below.

Learning Outcomes for Module 1

- Identify the main components of excellent customer service
- Demonstrate an understanding of the importance of customer service to an organisation's reputation and success
- Understand the role of the Manager or Team Leader in leading a team to achieve excellent customer service
- Identify rules, including legislation, codes of practice and organisational procedures that should be followed by a customer service team

Learning Outcomes for Module 2

- Understand the purpose of an organisation's Mission, Vision and Objectives
- Understand the function of an organisation's Customer Service Strategy
- Recognise how individual and team performance objectives can be derived from overall organisational objectives for customer service
- Identify a range of effective methods of communicating objectives in a team

Learning Outcomes for Module 3

- Recognise the distinguishing features of a Customer Focused Team
- Distinguish between internal and external customers
- Recognise effective methods of gathering and using feedback from customers
- Understand how Service Standards are used to help in the delivery of excellent customer service

Learning Outcomes for Module 4

- Recognise the key features of a customer focused approach to the organisation of human resources in a team
- Identify the key features of Emotional Intelligence in relation to customer service
- Identify appropriate organisational structures for a customer service team
- Recognise the importance of systems and processes for the delivery of excellent customer service

Learning Outcomes for Module 5

- Identify key features of communication in a customer focused team
- Recognise how motivation can be achieved in a team
- Understand how empowerment and delegation can be used by Managers or Team Leaders to contribute to the delivery of excellent customer service
- Recognise the key aspects of equality and diversity that impact upon customer service
- Recognise how reward and recognition arrangements in a team can contribute to the delivery of excellent customer service

Learning Outcomes for Module 6

- Understand how to listen to customers in order to identify potential and actual problems
- Identify the key steps to defusing potentially difficult situations
- Identify appropriate action to resolve customer service problems
- Understand the importance of learning from customer service problems

Learning Outcomes for Module 7

- Identify the main features of change in an organisation
- Identify typical Barriers to Change
- Understand key tactics to assist a Manager or Team Leader in achieving desired changes
- Show an understanding of the importance of Service Partnerships in a team delivering excellent customer service

Learning Outcomes for Module 8

- Understand the role of innovation in helping a team to deliver excellent customer service
- Recognise the importance of keeping to the rules when improving customer service
- Understand how technology may be used to improve service for customers

Learning Outcomes for Module 9

- Recognise the importance of Leadership in inspiring teams to deliver excellent customer service
- Show an understanding of an effective model for Personal and Professional Development of customer related skills and knowledge

0.5   Your Personal Objectives

WORK-BASED ACTIVITY

Your Personal Objectives

To start with, think about what you hope to get out of this development programme.   Where in your Customer Service Management or Team Leading role do you need to improve your own understanding and skills? Decide on your personal objectives which will enable you to improve your performance as a Customer Service Manager or Team Leader. Write in the space below up to five personal objectives for your development programme.

1
2
3
4
5

0.6   Progression to Further Learning

This Best Practice Guide for Customer Service Managers will equip you with the knowledge and understanding you need to lead and build a customer focused team. Once you have completed it, you could consider moving onto further learning and qualifications:

- An online course in Implementing a Customer Service Strategy
- A Certificate or Diploma in Management, enhancing your understanding of Management concepts and skills
- A vocational qualification relevant to your specific employment sector

1   Managers and Customer Service Excellence

Welcome to Module 1 of the Best Practice Guide for Customer Service Managers. In this module we look at the importance of excellent customer service and what it comprises. You will consider the role of the Manager or Team Leader in contributing to the success of your organisation, through the delivery of excellent customer service.

1.1   Learning Outcomes

Learning Outcomes for Module 1
On successful completion of this module you should be able to: • Identify the main components of excellent customer service • Demonstrate an understanding of the importance of customer service to an organisation's reputation and success • Understand the role of the Manager or Team Leader in leading a team to achieve excellent customer service • Identify rules, including legislation, codes of practice and organisational procedures that should be followed by a customer service team

1.2   Who are Our Customers?

Let's be clear from the start who we mean by "customers." They could be any of a range of people or organisations.

- External Customers – individuals, end-users or consumers of a product or service – these are outside your own organisation

- Internal Customers - individuals, departments or sub-groups within your own organisation

- Corporate Customers - organisations that your own organisation does business with – such as suppliers, distribution companies or transport providers (These are also external customers, as they too are outside your own organisation)

Customers' Perceptions

As a Manager or Team Leader, you are probably already aware of the importance of "what the customer thinks." In other words, one of your key objectives for your team should be to maintain or improve the customer's perception of the services received from the team and the whole organisation.

Customers make judgements about an organisation based upon their experience of that organisation, its products, its service and its people. A single customer's experience may be only a brief encounter, perhaps when a product is being ordered from a supplier, bought in a shop, by telephone or perhaps ordered through a website. Whatever the situation, what counts is the Customer Experience – the service that the customer perceives, rather than the service the organisation thinks it has delivered. The best way of organising your team around customers is to be in touch with the Customer Experience.

1.3   What Does Customer Service Comprise?

Now we need to look at Customer Service and what it actually comprises. Here is a definition.

> **DEFINITION**
>
> ### Customer Service
>
> Customer Service is the sum total of what an organisation does to meet customer expectations and produce customer satisfaction.

Think about the definition and relate it to your own and your team's work with customers. The actual services that a customer receives will vary from one situation to another. The combination of services that you deliver to customers depends upon a number of factors:

- The core product or service being delivered
- The organisation delivering the service
- The individual delivering the service
- The customer receiving the service
- The specific point or stage in the Customer Transaction that has been reached

Service is provided at various Touch-Points during a customer's relationship with an organisation – this relationship could last for years, especially for your organisation's valuable, long-standing customers. In addition, there are different aspects of service provided at different times during a customer transaction, such as before, during and after a purchase.

*The combination of services that you deliver to customers
depends upon.. the individual delivering the service..*

This applies to internal customers, as well as external customers. If, for example, a service is being provided to an internal customer this could be before, during or after a particular task was set.

Remember also that the service itself might actually be provided by different means.

- Service can be provided by a person, such as a customer orders assistant, a logistics operator or a retail assistant

- Service can provided by automated systems such as E-Commerce (or self-service) websites, or automated telephone response systems

Some customers may prefer a human interaction to an automated or self-service interaction. Organisations need to choose carefully the type of interaction they are going to provide at these touch-points – and this will depend on costs to some extent. Indeed, customers do not necessarily reject automated services. Some world-renowned online retailers have established their global reputations by delivering very high levels of service through automated sales and service systems. Whatever the particular channel that your organisation uses for delivering its customer service, it is essential that the quality and reliability is as high as possible and that you know what your customers think of the services they receive.

Service Characteristics

Customers who do business with you have high expectations. They expect as a minimum that you will deliver the Core Product or Core Service to the appropriate specifications and quality. The correct items should be delivered, as ordered, to the right destination and at the right time. In the case of a core service, that must also be provided as agreed - often within a Service Level Agreement or contract.

But what exactly do your own customers expect? It is important for you and your team to analyse the detailed service characteristics that you deliver to customers. Think carefully about the range of service characteristics that your team provides.

DEFINITION

Service Characteristics

Service characteristics are the individual elements that make up the service provided to customers

Service Characteristics can be grouped under the following seven headings, with examples given below.

Reliability

For example:

- The quality attached to a product
- Prompt delivery of an item
- Correct numbers of products requested in a delivery

Competence

For example:

- Efficient packaging of a number of items in a delivery
- Efficient delivery and unloading of items at the customer's premises
- Being an accurate advisor to customers

Responsiveness

For example:

- Service recovery processes in the case of problems, with adequate compensation, if appropriate
- Responding to internal customers' needs on time
- Helping internal customers resolve problems and difficulties

To give an example, a distinctive and successful Service Offer was provided by a solicitor. The company wanted to differentiate itself from other solicitors by offering a Home Advice Service. It recognised that some customers preferred the convenience of discussing their legal requirements in their own home, rather than always travelling to the centre of the town where the company was based. Home visits proved a successful Service Offer and many new clients were attracted to do business with the company. The extra business generated made up for the increased cost of travelling to clients' homes, customers valued the accessibility of the service and found the solicitor more approachable.

Non-competitive organisations also benefit from designing and building the right Service Offer for their customers. For instance, the Service Offer of a health authority is vitally important for its patients. Service characteristics such as accessibility, reliability and understanding customers can be just as critical in the eyes of patients as the actual health treatment itself. It is common for health authorities to Benchmark their Service Offer against other health authorities, trying to build a Service Offer which is as good, if not better than other, similar health authorities.

WORK-BASED ACTIVITY

Adding to Your Service Offer

Analyse the Service Offer of your own team or organisation. Use the information from the previous activity in which you gave examples of the service characteristics that your team or organisation is responsible for. Now try to think of what you could add to your Service Offer, in order to improve the service for customers, and also to build a Service Offer which is distinctive in your own sector or market place.

Additions to Our Service Offer:

Changing the Service Offer

Organisations have processes for changing their Service Offer, and you as the Manager or Team Leader must keep to these processes if you intend to make changes to your own Service Offer. Within a typical process, it is important to find out from customers themselves what they want and expect from your organisation. Just as important when designing or changing the Service Offer is to ensure that any increased costs of delivering services in a new way are justified, and that employees have the knowledge, skills and support to deliver the services effectively and consistently.

1.4 Customers Are Key

Customers' Expectations are increasing. Your organisation probably has competitors who are trying to improve their own Service Standards in order to exceed their customers' expectations. Your organisation (and therefore your team) needs to do the same, but better. Because today's customers are so demanding, it is only those organisations which recognise rising customer expectations, and continuously go the extra step to satisfy and delight their customers, that will succeed. Customers, then, are key for you and your team.

Customers' expectations are increasing

Figure 1, Increasing Customer Expectations, shows three different levels of service that can be provided for customers. The three levels of service that an organisation can provide are described below.

Core Service – this will provide the basic products and services, and will meet some customers' expectations. It is unlikely to satisfy other customers who have experienced better service elsewhere. This could be through the purchase of an entirely different product or service. Today's customers remember the best service they have received (or heard about), and demand that level of service from all their transactions, regardless of the product or sector. If you continue to offer just core service, it is likely that customers will move to competitors before too long.

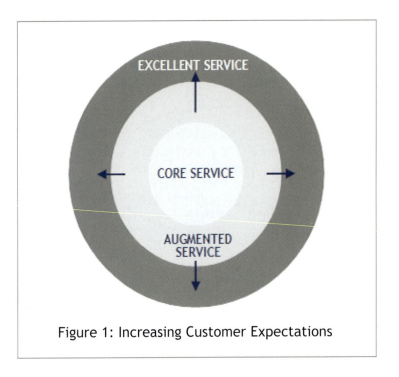

Figure 1: Increasing Customer Expectations

Augmented Service – this goes beyond core service and is the minimum your organisation should provide in order to at least keep up with the market. You will generally be meeting and exceeding customers' expectations. Augmented Service will retain many customers in the short and medium term, but this level of service does not consistently deliver really exceptional experiences for customers - the "Wow!" factor is not there all the time.

Excellent Service – this means that your organisation is maximising its chances of being the market leader, constantly innovating to find new ways of exceeding customer expectations, with highly skilled and motivated individuals delivering exceptional service to customers. You are consistently attempting to exceed customers' expectations - every time a customer interaction takes place. This level of service really does consistently deliver the "Wow!" factor.

Find new ways of exceeding customer expectations

GCU Finance – Levels of Service

Sandra Gonzales, GCU's Director of Customer Service, has carried out an of assessment customer service at one of its European Banks. This was done by holding several focus groups, to which some of the bank's customers were invited. The customers were asked to compare Gnu's services to what they knew of other banks. Here are some typical customer comments:

- "My account is generally managed well, and I am really pleased with the way they deal with my queries over the telephone."

- "When I switched to GCU from my previous bank I was pleasantly surprised at the level of customer service."

- "They may not be the best bank, but I've found them better than I expected them to be."

- "I have heard of another bank whose service for customers is really amazing, but nevertheless I am very happy I opened an account with GCU."

◉ Select the best answer to the question:

Which level of service is GCU Finance providing for its customers?

A ○   Core Service

B ○   Augmented Service

C ○   Excellent Service

1.9 Knowing and Following Your Organisation's Rules

It is critical that your organisation's processes, rules and regulations are followed. Here are some guide-lines on following processes.

GUIDE-LINE
Following Organisational Processes

Organisational Procedures Relating to Your Manager or Team Leader Role

Customer service, as with any business activity, must be conducted according to your organisation's rules, guidelines and expectations. It should also be delivered in such a way as to fit with the broader objectives that your organisation has for customer service, such as in a statement of organisational values, strategic objectives or a Credo. Find out how others deliver excellent service and adopt their best practices wherever you can.

Laws

There are key laws which you must ensure that your team keeps to. The laws that are relevant to you depend partly on the sector you are working within, but there are some key areas of legislation which apply to all or most organisations. Check the laws applying to:

- Consumer Rights and Consumer Protection relating to selling goods and services
- Data Protection and Freedom of information
- Sex Discrimination
- Equality and Diversity
- Disability Discrimination
- Health and Safety
- Human Rights
- Copyright
- Any other aspects specific to your sector or industry

The Internet is a good source of information and advice on these and other laws. Be sure to confirm the reliability of the specific websites that you use by cross-checking with others and by examining in detail the sources of the information given and the originators of the website. In addition, check any information you obtain against your own organisation's publications and processes, making absolutely certain that you as the Manager or Team Leader are using and giving the correct advice to your team.

Following Organisational Processes (continuation)

Even laws are open to interpretation. One particular term that you will come across in relation to several laws is the word "reasonable." For example, in the UK's Disability Discrimination Act (1995), employers have a duty to make **reasonable** adjustments where physical features of their premises or arrangements place a disabled person at a substantial disadvantage compared to a non-disabled person. In relation to Health and Safety, organisations have a duty to take **reasonable** care of the workforce by providing (where relevant) safe plant and machinery, employing competent staff and providing safe systems of work.

The word reasonable allows those who enforce or uphold the law to use discretion according to the circumstances; you should view **reasonable** as what a well-informed person or organisation would be expected to do according to today's standards of behaviour. Ensure that you talk to others and reach a consensus in your organisation about how these laws require you to organise services and facilities for both external and internal customers.

Rules and Regulations

Ensure that you and your team keep within the rules when delivering service to customers, and more broadly in the operation and management of customer relationships. In addition to the legal considerations, you should ensure that you know all about service level agreements and contract terms that will affect how you must work with your customers. There are often important rules which affect, for example, how to capture, record, manipulate and pass on customer data, and these will usually cover both commercial confidentiality and the protection of personal data.

Know and Communicate the Rules

An essential point to realise is that it is your own responsibility as a Manager or Team Leader working with customers, to ensure you have a thorough knowledge of relevant legislation and rules. For example, if you travel to your customer's premises for a planning meeting or focus group discussion, make yourself aware of, and abide by that organisation's rules - such as for health and safety or commercial confidentiality. Spread the message throughout your team, and reinforce it regularly at meetings and team activities.

1.10 End-of-Module Knowledge-Check

KNOWLEDGE-CHECK 1.4

⊙ Select the best answer to the question:

1 Customer Service is often defined as:

A O Everything an organisation does to meet the needs of its stakeholders

B O Everything an organisation does to meet customers' expectations and produce customer satisfaction

C O What an organisation supplies in addition to its normal range of products

2 Prompt delivery of an item to a customer is an example of a Service Characteristic known as:

A O Reliability

B O Accessibility

C O Professionalism

3 Core Service is a level of service which:

A O Provides a high standard of service delivery

B O Is likely to satisfy most customers

C O Provides only the basic products and services

4 Team Synergy is:

A O A team gaining by working well together

B O A team's approach to customers

C O A team's policy on internal Customer Service

5 Customer Service should be conducted according to:

A O Individual preferences

B O The individual employee's approach to handling customer transactions

C O Your organisation's rules, guidelines and expectations

2   Setting and Communicating Objectives

Introduction

Welcome to Module 2 of the Best Practice Guide for Customer Service Managers. In this module we look at how an organisation's mission and vision for customer service are translated into a strategy. You will see the importance of communicating the organisation's aims and of setting individual objectives for your team which are linked to the strategy. You will have the opportunity to translate the Customer Service Strategy into clear objectives and targets for every member of your team.

2.1   Learning Outcomes

Learning Outcomes for Module 2
On successful completion of this module you should be able to: • Understand the purpose of an organisation's Mission, Vision and Objectives   • Understand the function of an organisation's Customer Service Strategy   • Recognise how individual and team performance objectives can be derived from overall organisational objectives for customer service   • Identify a range of effective methods of communicating objectives in a team

2.2   Why Have Objectives?

It is important to be clear about the objectives that are set for your team. If you do not have clear and well-communicated objectives, you and your team risk not knowing:

• Where you are going

• What you have achieved

• Whether your achievements fit with your organisation's plans

• Whether you and your team are delivering customer satisfaction

For consistently excellent customer service to be possible, organisations need clear, well communicated objectives that identify the importance that the whole organisation attaches to customer service. The exact place of customer service within these objectives depends very much on the specific organisation. However, it is certainly true that all organisations with a reputation for excellent service have not got to that position by chance. They have created a vision for excellent service and then been determined and skilled in designing the appropriate structures, frameworks and measures in order to realise the vision.

It is also important to realise that the organisation's goal of customer service excellence is just one (albeit a vitally important one) of a number of organisational objectives. The organisation must balance customer service against other objectives, which may concern, for example:

- The organisation's finances
- The organisation's plans for dealing with competitors
- Constraints on the organisation's resources
- Plans to develop new products and services

Excellent customer service comes at a cost. It is a cost worth paying, because of the now over-riding importance that customers attach to the service received in choosing which organisations to do business with. However, the organisation's resources are limited, and it is part of your responsibility as a manager not only to help implement the organisation's objectives, but also to understand how to balance your team's own needs and capabilities against the needs and expectations of customers.

Self Assessment - Team Customer Focus

Check whether your team is competent to deliver world class service excellence. This activity will help you to identify your areas of strength and weakness. Once you have completed it, go on to make your initial plans in the Team Action Plan.

⦿ Select Yes or No	Yes	No

STRATEGY AND CULTURE:

		Yes	No
Commitment	Does the team have a clear commitment and plan to deliver excellent customer service?	○	○
Credibility	Does the team keep its promises to its customers?	○	○

PEOPLE:

		Yes	No
Capability	Are the team's people recruited, trained and developed to be excellent providers of customer service?	○	○
Continuity	Do your methods of rewarding and recognising the team focus on excellent customer service?	○	○

PROCESSES:

		Yes	No
Consistency	Do the team's processes focus on consistent delivery of service for customers?	○	○
Creativity	Does the team have a culture of continuous improvement and innovation?	○	○

Identify Your Key Issues from this Self Assessment:

WORK-BASED ACTIVITY

Team Action Plan

Now you need to plan your areas for change.

- Write below the actions that you intend to take over the coming weeks and months
- Share the plans with your team ensuring they support the changes needed, and understand the benefits they will bring and their own role in making them happen
- Keep a check on your actions by reviewing them regularly at your team meetings
- Record the progress that you and your team make with your Team Action Plan

Action Completed	Progress Made	Date
1		
2		
3		
4		
5		

2.3 Organisational Vision, Mission and Values

Ensure that you know and fully understand your organisation's aims for customer service excellence. Without that understanding you will not be able to fully translate these aims into actions for your own team and yourself as Manager or Team Leader.

Organisational Aims

Your organisation's aims and objectives have been set by the owners, directors or other stakeholders of the organisation. These aims and objectives may include customers – describing perhaps the type and level of service that your organisation wants to give its customers.
An organisation often states its aims, objectives and values in the form of a Vision Statement, a Mission Statement or a set of Organisational Values.

Purpose of Organisational Aims

Visions, mission statements and stated organisational values have several purposes:

- To ensure the organisation is going in the direction that its owners, directors and other stakeholders want

- To inform a range of stakeholders, such as employees, customers, shareholders and partners, about where the organisation is heading

- To give employees of the organisation a sense of direction within their everyday work, responsibilities and targets

Vision Statements

Visions and Missions

Many organisations publish their vision or mission statements on their website and often in annual reports. The vision describes a future identity – what it wants to be at some stage in the future - and the mission describes what the organisation will do to achieve that vision.

DEFINITION

Vision

A Vision Statement describes where an organisation aspires to be in the future. It may describe how the organisation sees itself over a period of 5 or 10 years if everything goes to plan. Some of the most successful organisations refer to customers within their vision statement.

DEFINITION

Mission

A Mission Statement describes the broad purpose for an organisation being in existence. It serves as an ongoing guide without a time frame. An organisation's mission can remain the same for many years if it has been well thought-out.

To see the difference between the definitions above, "We help transport goods and people efficiently and cost effectively without damaging the environment" is an example of a mission statement; "We will be one amongst the top three transporters of goods and people in Europe by 2012" is a vision statement. The vision is a concrete and unambiguous goal. Look at the examples of vision statements below.

BEST PRACTICE

Unicentro - Vision

Our vision is of a world in which everyone, irrespective of nationality, culture, class or education, can enjoy the benefits of a pleasurable, exciting and safe retail experience. This vision is at the heart of our determination to be the most successful global retail services provider.

BEST PRACTICE

Euro-Deporte - Vision

Sport and leisure as a human occupation is unrivalled in its potential benefits for health and happiness. Euro-Deporte is committed to the integrated and sustainable management of buildings and spaces dedicated to fun and health.

By 2015 we will have established successful centres in every country in Europe and the Americas, all of which will have state of the art equipment and be built on the three cornerstones of Customer Satisfaction, Energy Efficiency and Shareholder Value.

Now review these examples of mission statements.

BEST PRACTICE
GCU Finance - Mission

- Working in partnership with our customers, we help them achieve their objectives for their personal and business finances
- Innovation for customers is the lifeblood of GCU, on which we will continue to build our reputation and success
- We shall create an environment where people love to work, a community of people who feel valued and inspired to deliver great customer service

BEST PRACTICE
Unicentro - Mission

We aim to …

- Provide maximum choice of products
- Offer value for money
- Be passionate about customers
- Provide a simple, fast, convenient and safe shopping experience

KNOWLEDGE-CHECK 2.1
GCU Finance – its Vision

Sandra Gonzales, GCU's Director of Customer Service, is answering a question from a Customer Service Manager about GCU's vision. Which of the following statements do you think is part of GCU's vision?

⊙   Select the best answer to the question:

A ○   Innovation for customers is the lifeblood of GCU, on which we will continue to build our reputation and success

B ○   GCU will be one of the three the largest European financial companies in Europe by 2012

C ○   GCU will become more customer-oriented in the years ahead

What really matters about visions and missions is that they are communicated effectively to everybody concerned – customers, employees and stakeholders. Organisational aims and objectives give employees, customers, managers and other stakeholders a sense of direction. They should mean something real to everyone.

Organisational Values

Many successful organisations publish written descriptions of their organisational values. These tend to describe the purpose and mission of the organisation, as well as its objectives and approach to the future.

DEFINITION

Organisational Values

Organisational values (or corporate values) are statements about the basic principles that an organisation and its employees intend to uphold. They may include standards for how customers will be treated. The values (which sometimes include ethical values) are normally communicated across the organisation to its employees, its customers and other stakeholders.

Organisations which understand the importance of customers in building business and customer loyalty have realised that it is essential to tell customers, employees, managers, and other stakeholders how customers will be satisfied. Of course, not all organisations write down their objectives in a formal way. Some smaller organisations do not publicise their overall purpose, aims or objectives. However, it is very important that you, as a Customer Service Manager or Team Leader, understand where your organisation is heading, and how it intends to get there.

Compare the vision and mission statements that you have already looked at with the following statement of organisational values.

BEST PRACTICE
Euro-Deporte – Organisational Values

Our Philosophy:

We aim to exceed our customers' expectations by providing an innovative approach to customer service. To stay at the front of this dynamic and rapidly moving industry, we constantly develop new ideas and services for our customers. These do not always come from the top and we rely on people throughout the business to maintain our high standards. By incorporating new ideas and new technologies, we have created a stimulating and rewarding environment for all of our employees. Our philosophy is best summed up in Our Five Fundamental Rules.

Our Five Fundamental Rules:

At Euro-Deporte everything we do is based on our 'five fundamental rules'. The rules speak for themselves and need little embellishment. However, it is worth stressing that the rules are applied not just in our stores, but in our call centres and support functions too, to ensure that we provide the best possible customer experience.

1. We are passionate about getting things right for customers
2. Nothing is gained by winning an argument but losing a customer
3. Always deliver what we promise. If in doubt, under-promise and over-deliver
4. The reputation of the whole company is in the hands of each employee
5. If we don't look after the customer, someone else will

Because you and your team members are concerned with customer service, you should be clear about how your organisation intends to improve or maintain its relationships with customers. Customers who are within your organisation – internal customers – are just as important as external customers. If your role is mainly in dealing with internal customers, you need a clear view on how your team can deliver high levels of service to them. One way of seeing this is that you are your external customers' ambassador within your own organisation.

WORK-BASED ACTIVITY

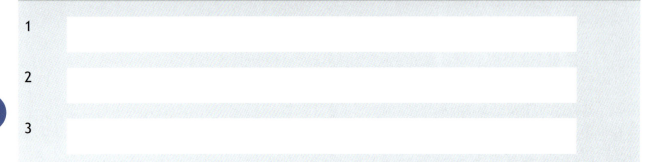

Your Organisational Values

Review the definition of Organisational Values, and the example from Euro-Deporte. Now write a simple set of organisational values for your own team. Remember that the purpose is to ensure that all team members are aware of the team's basic principles – especially the standards for how customers will be treated.

Write three statements which could form Organisational Values for your own team.

1

2

3

Customer Charter

Another way for organisations to communicate information about their services and values to their customers and stakeholders is through a Customer Charter. Look at this one from Unicentro.

BEST PRACTICE

Unicentro – Customer Charter

We always aim to:

- Deal with you honestly, fairly and politely
- Give you the information you need
- Try to see things from your point of view
- Respect your right to confidentiality
- Be trustworthy and reliable
- Take account of peoples' individual needs

Comments, complaints and suggestions:

- We are always happy to receive feedback from our customers on the services we provide
- We have an easy to use complaints procedure if things do go wrong

47

WORK-BASED ACTIVITY

What are Your Organisation's Objectives?

Find out about the objectives of your own organisation.   If they are published, summarise the mission and/or vision statements. Note whether they talk about customers. If your organisation does not have written-down statements about its aims, objectives and values, describe what you think are its actual aims and objectives.

Aims and Objectives:

How clear are the organisational aims and objectives?

How will you translate these into actions for your own team?

2.4   Customer Service Strategy

Consider this definition of a Customer Service Strategy:

DEFINITION

Customer Service Strategy

A Customer Service Strategy is a high-level plan that communicates to everyone involved with an organisation how it will develop relationships with its customers in order to maximise customer satisfaction and customer loyalty, and achieve business success.

An effective Customer Service Strategy is a common feature of organisations that provide excellent service to their customers. It forms part of an organisation's Customer Service Framework – the means by which it will achieve excellent service provision for both internal and external customers. However, a consistently high level of customer service does not happen by accident. Without a clear strategy, spelling out how the organisation intends to maintain and develop its customer relationships, it is unlikely to be able to keep customers loyal in the long term.

The Purpose of a Customer Service Strategy

Some of your customers may be key, high-value partners with whom your organisation has held successful, long-standing relationships. There is no room for complacency regarding these long-standing partners. Even what appear to be the strongest relationships are not safe from competitors. Your organisation will undoubtedly face stiff competition from others who are constantly looking to find new ways to exceed customers' expectations. Without an effective customer service strategy this could allow your key partners to be tempted away by competitors' offers of better and more innovative customer service. And the customer service strategy is not simply an internal plan that is cascaded through a business. It is also your organisation's plan for gaining a winning advantage over its competitors.

Pulling in the Same Direction

The Customer Service Strategy enables everyone in the organisation to see the road ahead for customer service. All employees can pull together in the same direction, with the same objectives in view. Managers, Team Leaders and Customer Service Professionals working together can identify and put into place the policies and procedures that will benefit customers. Resources can be secured and allocated so that the component parts of the strategy can be implemented, and the objectives achieved.

Communicating the Strategy

Through the Customer Service Strategy, everybody in the organisation, from customer-facing service staff to leaders of the organisation, will be able to understand their own roles and responsibilities when dealing with customers. Of course, a Customer Service Strategy will only work if it is well communicated. It needs to be explained and understood by all concerned. It must then be implemented effectively. Your responsibility as a Manager or Team Leader is to recognise not only the overall intentions of your organisation, but also your own role in contributing to the success of the Customer Service Strategy.

Strategy Components

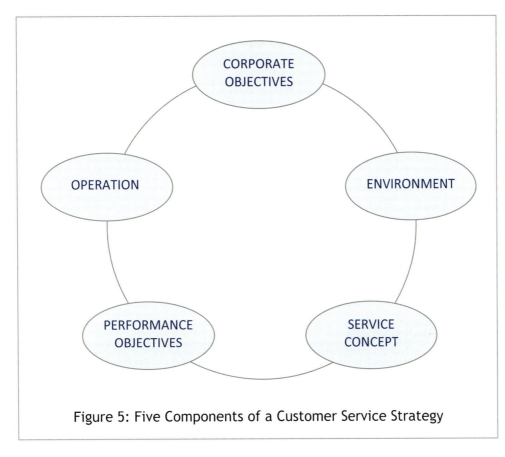

Figure 5: Five Components of a Customer Service Strategy

What does an effective Customer Service Strategy look like? It will generally include the five components shown in Figure 5:

- Corporate objectives
- Environment
- Service Concept
- Performance Objectives
- Operation

Corporate Objectives

Corporate Objectives state in clear terms what the organisation is intending to achieve regarding customer service and customer relationships. The objectives can be motivational in themselves. They spell out the excellent service and value that the organisation wants to deliver for its customers. The objectives often also set out the changes that will need to be made, and a timeframe for their achievement. It is helpful to publicise an organisation's corporate objectives – for example in its promotional literature and on its website. This allows its stakeholders, including customers, partners and employees, to see where the organisation is heading.

Environment

The strategy is built partly on the basis of the organisation's external environment. This enables the customer service strategy to be responsive to a number of factors, including:

- Changes in the industry or sector
- Changing customer tastes and expectations
- Technological changes
- The behaviour and plans of competitors, including how competitors are likely to react to the intended changes

BEST PRACTICE
Unicentro – Customer Service Strategy and Environment

Unicentro was aware of the threat from competitors to its contracts with long-standing retailers. In order to develop its Customer Service Strategy it firstly analysed its external environment.

Unicentro identified that one of its main competitors was planning changes in the way it designed and developed its retail centres. In order to stay a step ahead of this competitor, Unicentro responded by including within its Customer Service Strategy a clear process for managing its customers' experiences. Every retailer that it does business with would be allocated to a Customer Relationship Manager. That Manager would have the responsibility of maintaining and building the customer relationship, maximising business with the retailer and ensuring a high level of customer satisfaction.

Service Concept

This important part of the Customer Service Strategy spells out the service that the organisation wants to provide for its customers. This helps the whole organisation – and its customers – focus on what the organisation intends to achieve. Some customer focused organisations include the

Service Concept in a credo which employees use as guide for their work with customers – for example, this one from a South American insurance company: "We are not just concerned with customer care - we call it 'Amazing Customer Service' - we go beyond what you get everywhere else." The company finds that its employees can relate to the concept very clearly, and it guides the rest of the Customer Service Strategy.

Performance Objectives

Performance objectives translate the Corporate Objectives into specific targets. Performance Objectives will be set for each operational area of the organisation in the form of targets and priorities. They enable the day to day activities of the organisation's people, working with customers, to contribute to the overall Customer Service Strategy. Performance Objectives are critical for you in your own work with customers. They should be kept under constant review, to check that all the work within your team is aligned with the overall direction of the organisation in achieving a consistently high level of customer service.

Operation

The design of an appropriate Operation (or Operational Plan) can be a complex activity. It may involve a large number of interrelated decisions that connect processes, employees and customers. New investment might be needed, or there could be a need to redeploy existing resources. The Operational Plan then needs to be checked against the objectives to ensure that the whole customer service strategy is consistent – and that it will achieve the objectives that have been set.

KNOWLEDGE-CHECK 2.2
Unicentro – Translating the Corporate Objectives

Unicentro has already established its Mission, Vision and Corporate Objectives, and is continuing to develop its Customer Service Strategy. James Wright-Smith, Unicentro's Senior Manager for Planning and Research, wants to align the day-to-day work of Unicentro's people to its Corporate Objectives. What is the best way to do this?

⊙   Select the best answer to the question:

A ○   Set Performance Objectives for each team
B ○   Write a Credo for the organisation
C ○   Analyse the organisation's external environment

2.5   Team Objectives

Some organisations have a two-way process so that communication on key decisions is bottom-up as well as top-down. Don't wait to be told about the top-down objectives; establish your own at team level which reflect your organisation's mission. Make sure they are in harmony with what your customers need and what your resources allow you to deliver. Check the team's objectives regularly to ensure that everyone still has a clear focus on what they are working towards, both individually and as a team.

2.6   Individual Objectives

Organisational, team and individual objectives should be in place, as shown in Figure 6. Set objectives for your team members. People like to have clear objectives and targets. They help you and your team to prioritise on the factors that matter most to customers. Objectives for all your team will give them a sense of motivation, and they will all be able to move in the same direction.

Figure 6: Organisational, Team and Individual Objectives

Objectives for individuals should:

- Relate to an area of responsibility such as improving a service
- Be set by discussion between those setting the objectives and those working to them
- Be agreed with those working towards them – this is not always possible but very desirable

Setting individual objectives for every team member is very important. People generally like to be included and they will realise, if they have clear individual objectives, that you as the Manager or Team Leader have carefully considered their role. They will see how they can contribute to the overall objectives of the team and the success of your organisation. Having individual objectives in place will also help you when assessing your team members' performance – for example when conducting appraisal reviews – and you will be able to discuss and plan areas for improvement.

Objectives for individuals should not be set by the Manager or Team Leader alone. Instead, try to jointly develop your team's objectives by seeking and inviting ideas and through discussion and negotiation. Ask your team members what they think their objectives should be. Do this in a One-To-One meeting with each team member (such as an appraisal review) and finish the meeting with an agreement on the objectives for the next period.

Use SMART objectives

Your SMART objectives should be:

- Specific: they are clear and precise for those working towards them
- Measurable: so you can tell whether you have got there or not, and what progress has been made
- Achievable: they should actually be within reach and not just a "wish list"
- Realistic: they really do describe what needs to be done in your organisation/team
- Time-constrained: they say what should be achieved by when

WORK-BASED ACTIVITY
Setting SMART Objectives

Set some objectives – either for the whole team or for a team member. Ensure they are all SMART.

Write three SMART objectives.

1

2

3

2.7   Communicating the Objectives

How many times have you heard people at work say: "They just don't communicate" - or: "They obviously don't talk to each other"? Communication is the root of many problems in organisations, and especially in teams.

Customer-Centric Communication

To help your team in its drive towards service excellence, encourage customer-centric communication. Communication should be effective both within and between teams. It needs to be effective also between different organisations.   You may deal with a range of supplier and customer organisations. Your customers and suppliers want a simple, customer focused way of doing business with you. They need to see you as a "joined up" team or organisation. They do not want to worry about the individual parts of an overall service. All parts of the service should fit together seamlessly for the customer. For your team this means in particular that your communication channels should be really open and effective.

Communication takes place up and down within an organisation and within a team. Pass to your team all the information they need about what your organisation is doing, and about other teams. Make sure that your team members' questions and concerns get fed upwards or into the right channels. Set up innovative systems for communicating at all levels in the team, and use technology to the full for this.

Communication Methods

Use a range of communication methods. There are so many to choose from, but it makes a big difference if you choose the right one for each purpose. Try to communicate using a method that is appropriate both for the task and the person you are communicating with. Remember all the ways that you can communicate with your staff, other teams, customers, visitors and others:

- One-to-ones
- Team briefings
- Informal chats
- Focus groups and Online Focus Groups
- Planning meetings
- Emails, letters and fax
- Notice-boards and newsletters
- Telephone and text messaging
- Websites
- Blogs (Weblogs) and social networking websites
- Promotional literature
- Customer evaluation sheets

Here is an example from GCU Finance of communicating organisational objectives:

BEST PRACTICE
GCU Finance – Communicating the Organisational Objectives

Communicating organisational objectives to employees:

- GCU makes it easy for customers to do business with them. They close the loop of listening to customers' frustrations, fixing those frustrations and so changing the way operations works.

- GCU's foundations were laid by a senior management team who were always involved with and accessible to staff. They developed an ethos where employees could fully identify with GCU's business values and objectives. (According to a recent survey, only about 15% to 20% of employees are fully engaged with what their company is trying to do).

- The managers in GCU's early days played an important part in ensuring that front line staff understood what the business stood for and the way it operated. Senior managers would attend every staff induction to emphasise the vision and purpose of the organisation. For example, their first HR director introduced a 6-week induction programme – when most companies in the sector inducted their staff over a period of only 2 weeks.

Training emphasised three things:

- Every customer is different
- First time problem resolution
- There are exceptions which staff must spend time to resolve

In the examples that you have looked at, the organisations make their own values very clear. Senior managers in those organisations believe that they, their staff and the design of their systems, are all guided by those values. The values can be seen as the lifeblood of the organisation – spreading throughout every part of the organisation.

KNOWLEDGE-CHECK 2.3
Euro-Deporte - Choosing Communication Methods

Henri Delotte, Customer Service Team Leader at a Euro-Deporte Fitness Centre, received several customer complaints recently. He has met with his team to discuss the complaints and how to deal with them. One of the team asked: "Let's find out from a representative range of customers what they think of our services, and if there are any other areas that could cause problems and complaints. What's the best way to do that?"

◉ Select the best answer to the question:

Which is the most appropriate communication method for Henri to advise?

A ○ One-to-ones with staff

B ○ Communicating with customers through Blogs

C ○ Focus groups involving customers

2.8   End-of-Module Knowledge-Check

KNOWLEDGE-CHECK 2.4

◉   Select the best answer to the question:

1   A vision statement normally describes:

    A O Why the organisation is in business

    B O The broad purpose of the organisation being in existence

    C O Where the organisation wants to be at some stage in the future

2   A Customer Service Strategy is a:

    A O Method of developing employees' customer based skills

    B O High level plan explaining how an organisation will build customer loyalty

    C O High level statement of an organisation's primary purpose

3   The element of a Customer Service Strategy which deals with changing customer tastes and expectations is called:

    A O Environment

    B O Operation

    C O Performance Objectives

4   When objectives are "SMART", the letter "A" is normally taken to stand for:

    A O Accessible

    B O Action related

    C O Achievable

5   Gaining feedback from a wide range of external customers would best be done through:

    A O Employee suggestion schemes

    B O Customer evaluation sheets

    C O Promotional literature

- Informal discussions

- Management meetings

- Employee surveys

- Employee suggestion schemes

- Internal customer questionnaires

- Intranet discussion boards

- Emails

- Telephone conversations

- Complaints

All of these feedback methods can be used for systematic gathering of information from internal customers. Look at the next Best Practice example showing where an employee survey has been used. Think about how this, or something similar, could be used in your own team or organisation to improve customer service.

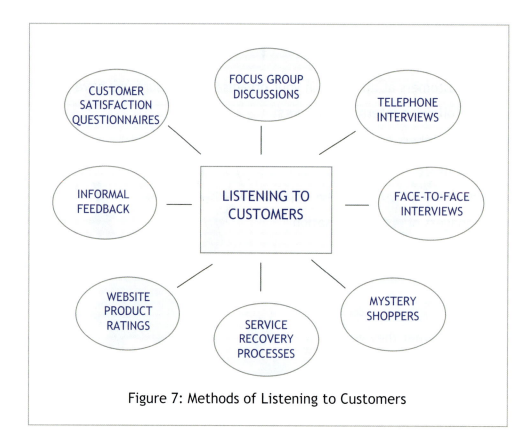

Figure 7: Methods of Listening to Customers

BEST PRACTICE
Euro-Deporte – Listening to Internal Customers

Euro-Deporte has built a culture of focus on internal customers - employees are treated as customers. Staff are regularly surveyed to identify any issues, so that managers can respond quickly. On a specific weekday in one region, a small sample of employees is selected for a "How are you?" survey. An email to them asks the question: "How are you feeling today?" Staff reply (anonymously) to say what their level of motivation is, how they are feeling and what is concerning them at the moment.

This gives managers in Euro-Deporte knowledge of the main issues are that are concerning staff. Managers can then take appropriate action, and this closes the loop between problem and solution. The survey also makes staff feel valued they can see that the organisation is listening to, and cares about their views. Senior management can gauge the overall motivation levels and find out about some of the key problems that might stand in the way of delivering excellent service to external customers.

KNOWLEDGE-CHECK 3.1
Listening to Customers

A Customer Focused Culture includes listening to customers – both internal and external. Which would be the most effective way listen to the views of internal customers?

◉   Select the best answer to the question:

A O   Website product ratings
B O   Employee surveys
C O   Informal feedback from sales transactions

Be the Eyes and Ears of Your Team

Decide exactly how to create that all-important customer focus in your team, so that the customer is at the heart of everything your team does. If you can achieve customer focus – which might require a change in your team's culture - you will find that customers will be permanently in your team members' thoughts. Every team briefing and informal discussion will raise questions such as, "What can we do to improve customer service?", "What impact will this have on the customer?" and, "How can we find out if that's what the customer wants?" This truly is a Customer Focused Culture.

Ensure that your team listens to your organisation. This might sound rather strange at first; however, poor communication is the root of many problems and difficulties in teams.

Communication can be difficult to get right, especially in larger and more dispersed organisations. You and your team must listen to your organisation, to find out, for example, what is wanted from top management, what the plans for the future are, and what are considered the key issues of the moment.

Your team relies on you, as the Manager or Team Leader, to be its eyes and ears. It is up to all individuals to keep up to date with the latest news across your organisation – and you can help by briefing the team about new initiatives, organisational changes and other issues, especially around customer service. Today's organisations are fast-moving, so expect changes on a day to day basis. Look out for the impact that changes are likely to have on your team, and communicate that clearly to your team members.

Be the Voice of Your Team

As well as acting as the team's eyes and ears, there will be times when you should act as the voice of your team. In your everyday work with team members you will pick up stories, issues, concerns and examples of good practice. Filter these - using your judgement - to select those points that need to be passed on. Find a way to feed the relevant issues up through your organisation, perhaps to your own manager, or through the management structure. Remember to communicate across your organisation too, with other teams, departments and managers where relevant.

No Blame Culture

If customers or your team members tell you about a difficulty they have had with another part of your organisation, pass the feedback on. Establish a no-blame culture in your team. If something goes wrong for a customer, use this as constructive feedback. Instead of seeing problems as purely negative you can turn it around and use problems as a way of keeping one step ahead. That way your team can learn from its mistakes, and thereby improve services for all your other customers. Complaints should be used in the same way – as a means of improving.

No blame culture

Customer Service Stories

Just as important as problems and challenges, pass on the good stories. Tell others in your organisation how a team member who is passionate about customer service has given a customer a really great experience. Maybe you have managed to delight customers by changing the way you work, or by introducing a new process. It could be just a small example of customer focus, but it can make all the difference. Act as your team's mouthpiece and you will help the whole organisation to learn quickly and respond to customers' changing needs.

3.6   Service Standards

Service Standards

We are familiar with standards and specifications for products. We know what to expect from a physical item such as DVD player, a tennis racket or a carton of orange juice. However, for services, which can seem less tangible there is a need to define for the customer the level and standard of service they can expect to receive. Service standards also have the benefit of reminding employees and managers of the levels of service they should be delivering for customers.

DEFINITION

Service Standards

Service standards are (fairly precise) descriptions of the levels of service that your customers can expect to receive. They describe the quality of service delivered, and are used by employees to guide them in their work with customers.

Service Standards are the operational standards that organisations commit to providing for their customers. They specify what the customer can expect and when. Service standards are useful for:

- Setting expectations with external and internal customers and colleagues
- Focusing organisations on the needs of the customer
- Ensuring consistency of service
- Providing a standard against which you can measure
- Encouraging service improvements

Service Standards provide measurable performance standards for customer service. They allow organisations to assess to what level specific service characteristics are actually delivered. Service standards can be specified in a contract, or other form of written agreement. These standards are a great help for you as the Service Provider, because they provide targets and monitoring tools as you deliver against your customer's needs.

It is likely that, in a contract or other form of written agreement, service standards will be mixed together with Product Standards. There is no need to separate the two – the first simply applies to your core services, and the second to your core products. Remember, though, that your service standards provide a valuable opportunity for your organisation to differentiate itself from the competition – through excellent customer service. And remember that customers' expectations of service are continually on the increase. As they experience better and more innovative service from others in your industry, and even from completely different industries across the world, they will raise their expectations of the service levels that you deliver.

BEST PRACTICE

Unicentro – Service Standards

Unicentro provides security services at all its retail centres. The customers – the retailers – have signed a Service Agreement written by Unicentro, which sets out the levels of service that Unicentro security guards will provide. Some of the service standards are shown below.

SERVICE STANDARDS:

Security provision	24 hours a day, 7 days a week
Security patrols	Constant during opening hours Every 30 minutes when centres are closed
Telephone response line	95% of calls answered within 4 rings
Emergency call-out response time	Arrival within 15 minutes of call-out
Customer satisfaction rate	At least 90% satisfaction with security services

Service Standards That Are Desirable and Achievable

Adopt a positive approach towards service standards. If such service standards are imposed by a customer without discussion, they can be seen by service providers as problematic from the start. They are much more effective when they have been discussed and agreed by both parties. That way, they closely reflect what is desirable and achievable.

Effective service standards should:

- Meet the business needs of the customer and be achievable for the service provider
- Be used to plan the operation of the service provider
- Enable both customer and service provider to monitor performance
- Be used to trigger corrective actions when they are in danger of not being met
- Be the subject of regular review within a planned contract review programme

Best practice when setting service standards is first to establish the needs of your customers. Both Quantitative Research (such as questionnaires and telephone surveys) and Qualitative Research (for example, customer focus groups and one to one interviews) are methods that can be used to identify the factors that are most important to customers. For example, one organisation in the automotive sector found that the five key areas of importance to customers were:

- Having named contacts

- Having a delivery and collection service

- Being informed of additional work and charges

- Accuracy of invoicing

- Quick problem solving

This data allowed the organisation to define service standards in each of these areas and then to monitor their performance with customers. Service standards can be defined in areas such as:

- Telephone responses

- Email responses

- Written responses

- Visits and meetings

- Appearance - of individuals and the environment

- Responses to complaints

Planning Service Standards

Service standards can de designed in a number of ways. Typical standards will relate to:

- **Timeliness**

  Services that you and your team provide for customers are often related to time. For example, your customers may want their calls to be answered within so many rings, have goods delivered to their business or house within a minimum number of days or have their complaints resolved within a specific time period.

- **Accuracy**

  Customers normally want the promise delivered. They expect their order to be 100% complete, rather than having to chase up on missing items. Therefore accuracy can be built into a service standard, letting the customer know that what was discussed, ordered and promised will be 100% correct.

- **Appropriateness**

  Appropriateness in service standards is about ensuring that customers' expectations have been met. It particularly applies to enquiries where the customer will be given information. The information and answers given must be appropriate to the enquiry, or else the customer's time will have been wasted. An example is where a customer makes an enquiry about a product through an organisation's e-commerce website. If the response is information about products that the customer did not ask about, then the service has not been appropriate for the situation.

Creating Service Standards

Decide whether organisational standards already exist. If they do, then your standards have already been created centrally, perhaps by senior managers and directors of your organisation. In this case your will need to interpret the standards with your own team, gain their commitment, and plan for how they will be met for your team.

Alternatively there may not be centrally created standards that apply to your team – or you may need additional ones. You will need to create your own standards at local level. Make sure that what you do fits with your organisation's objectives and strategies.

Use a range of sources to develop a set of standards for your team or organisation. They will probably include:

- Managers
- Team members
- Existing customers
- Potential new customers (who may "shop elsewhere" at the moment)
- Former customers who have gone to a competitor
- Competitors (research perhaps by a mystery shopper activity)

BEST PRACTICE
GCU Finance – Performance to the Service Standards

GCU Finance implements service standards for its personal account holders in its banks. One branch of the bank has recorded performance against the standards for customers coming into the bank or telephoning. (GCU Finance calls this part of its Service Standards "Responsiveness." It has additional Service Standards for monitoring other aspects of customer service). The teams responsible for the standards discuss the performance figures each month and then introduce improvements where necessary.

SERVICE STANDARD	PERFORMANCE IN PREVIOUS 2 MONTHS	
	Jan 2008	Feb 2008
See 100% of customers within 3 minutes of any pre-arranged appointment times	100%	100%
Letters and faxes answered within 2 working days	100%	100%
E-mail enquiries answered within 1 working day	86%	88%
100% of telephone calls answered within 20 seconds	93%	91%

Commitment to Service Standards

Ownership, visibility and commitment are absolutely key in implementing Service Standards. Your team, and many others in the organisation must come on board to make the standards deliverable.

Ownership

The Chief Executive (or head of the organisation), directors and senior managers should be sponsors and champions. They must "walk the talk", own the process and ensure on-going focus on standards in employee communications.

Visibility

"How well are we doing?" should be a question that employees don't have to ask. Customer Service Standards and the current performance against those standards should be communicated to all employees on a timely basis. Notice boards, memos, email, team briefings, newsletters and the organisation's intranet are appropriate methods. Team members will really appreciate the opportunity for discussion. Employees who are based out of the office are frequently overlooked, so they should receive special consideration.

Service Standards – Dos and Don'ts

DO:

- Gain commitment from all levels of management and staff for the standards
- Use standards as "specifications" of your services – rather like a product specification
- Use your standards to confirm that customers have received what they have been promised – and to identify any gaps in your services
- Base your standards on accurate customer research

DON'T:

- Have too many standards – standards "for everything" just end up being ineffective
- Include standards that cannot really be measured
- Make your standards ambiguous – they must be very precise and clear to customers and employees
- Forget to review your standards every so often – to make certain they are still up to date and relevant for your customers

Service Level Agreement

Organisations often publish their service standards as service level agreements. These help customers, suppliers and other partners to understand what levels of service to expect.

Service Level Agreement

A service level agreement (SLA) states, in measurable terms, the levels of service that an organisation will provide and a customer can expect to receive. Some SLAs also give details of what will happen if the organisation fails to meet its agreed levels of service.

Service Level Agreements (SLAs) can be useful for internal customer service as well. You may want to specify to other departments or functions in your organisation the levels of service they can expect. Think about getting a group within your team to develop an internal SLA.

BEST PRACTICE
GCU Finance – Service Level Agreement

GCU Finance is considering introducing a Service Level Agreement for its pensions customers:

- We aim to provide a high quality service to our customers at all times.
- When you contact us by letter, telephone, email or in person we will:
  - Send you a reply within 2 working days of receiving your communication
  - Answer your telephone calls within 3 rings
  - Identify ourselves by name in all communications
- If you have an appointment with a named person when visiting our offices, they will see you within 5 minutes of the arranged time.
- If you have not made an appointment, someone will see you within 10 minutes.
- If we visit you we will arrive at the appointed time. If there are any unavoidable delays we will call you at least 30 minutes before the appointment time to inform you of any delay.

3.7   Service Measurement

Measuring Customer Service

How well does your team's service meet standards? In order to move towards service excellence you will want, as a Manager or Team Leader, to assess whether, and to what extent, your team is delivering its Service Standards. Therefore you must have reliable and cost-effective methods of Service Measurement. Just as with your methods of listening to customers, you will need to measure both qualitative and quantitative aspects of your service delivery.

Base your measurements on Service Standards themselves where you can. Use technology wherever appropriate to collect reliable and meaningful information about how well your team is matching up to those standards. A particular feature when measuring Service Standards is that you need to look at two aspects: perception and reality. One method of measuring these two facets of customer service is known as Gap Analysis.

Gap Analysis

Design your data collection methods so that you can distinguish between perception and reality. The perceptions of customer service may include:

- How well your team members believe they are meeting the needs of customers
- How well managers in the organisation think that Service Standards are being kept to

The reality of customer service is determined by the views of the customers themselves, or by factual (quantitative) information:

* What customers actually think about your service delivery
* Whether customers believe that you have kept to your published Service Standards
* How well the quantitative information shows that measurable and quantifiable Service standards have been met

Measuring Customer Satisfaction

You have seen the importance of having satisfied customers. It is all too easy to assume that you are giving customers the services and products that they want. Start to think about how you determine your customers' levels of satisfaction. Identify your current methods of measuring Customer Satisfaction, and try to think of any gaps that could be leaving you with inadequate or inaccurate information about customers.

Remember that customer service as a whole includes a wide range of specific Service Characteristics. In most industries there are many Touch-Points where customer transactions take place. It is important to check on customers' perceptions of your service levels at each of these touch-points. Customer transactions often take place at different times, in different places and between different individuals. Sometimes the transactions are conducted using electronic communications systems, such as when customers place orders by email, or check on fulfilment progress through a website. Therefore it is important to build up an accurate picture of the overall satisfaction of your customers.

Use appropriate and reliable tools for measuring your customer satisfaction - try searching the internet for tools and methods for measuring customer satisfaction in the next Work-Based Activity.

Tools for Measuring Customer Satisfaction

Try these internet search terms to find ways of measuring customer satisfaction:

- Customer Satisfaction Measurement
- Customer Service Measurement
- Customer Satisfaction Index
- Customer Service Self Assessment

FINDINGS:

Summarise what you have found

APPLICATION:

How will you apply your findings to your own team?

Gap Analysis Tools

Amongst the many tools for measuring customer satisfaction, Gap Analysis is a good example. It enables organisations to measure their customer satisfaction rates against a set of service quality factors which are well established as being most important to the customer.

Reliability	The ability to perform the promised service dependably and accurately
Assurance	The knowledge and courtesy of the employees and their ability to convey trust and confidence
Tangibles	The physical facilities, equipment, personnel and communication materials
Empathy	The caring, individualised attention the organisation provides its customers
Responsiveness	The willingness to help customers and provide a prompt service

Gap Analysis uses interviews or questionnaires to capture employees' views on customer expectations. These are compared to the views of customers on the service they actually receive. The differences, or gaps, identify where the organisation needs to improve. In a similar way, the expectations of managers and of staff can be compared, showing up the gaps between the planned provision of customer service and the service that is actually delivered. Gaps here could lead to staff training, perhaps to resolve customer service problems more quickly, or to bring staff closer to their customers.

The Gap Analysis tool uses performance scores to measure customer satisfaction, and so these scores can also be used to benchmark performance. An organisation could plot improvements in customer satisfaction, or compare its performance to other, competing organisations.

4   Getting the Right People and Resources

Introduction

Welcome to Module 4. In this module we look at a customer focused approach to human resources, including the acquisition of Customer Based Skills. Emotional Intelligence is one area of skill and knowledge which could make a big difference to your team's delivery of customer service. You will also have the opportunity to review your physical resources, organisational structure and systems and processes in the light of the need for excellent customer service.

4.1   Learning Outcomes

Learning Outcomes for Module 4

On successful completion of this module you should be able to:

- Recognise the key features of a customer focused approach to the organisation of human resources in a team

- Identify the key features of Emotional Intelligence in relation to customer service

- Identify appropriate organisational structures for a customer service team

- Recognise the importance of systems and processes for the delivery of excellent customer service

4.2   What People and Resources are Needed?

We now need to consider the benefits of Customer Based Skills in your team, and how they can be acquired.

Benefits of Customer Based Skills

There are real advantages of having a team that is highly skilled in dealing with customers:

- Your team will be appropriately trained customer service professionals who consistently deliver service excellence at the customer interface

- Improved communication skills – to benefit customers, building good customer relationships, and providing customers with a single, effective point of contact

- Staff retention - they will be more motivated and committed to their job

- The team will develop a service personality and provide services tailored to customers' needs - "can-do" attitudes that benefit both internal and external customers

- Rapport within the team - they become one, supporting each other to deliver service excellence

- A culture of Continuous Improvement will develop, focused on meeting the needs of customers and anticipating their future requirements

- Happy staff will lead to happy customers – for example, the smiling disposition of the person answering the customer's call will be infectious

Acquiring and Developing Customer Based Skills

Look at the skills in your team. Match individuals' skills to your team job roles, and make sure that you have the skills, knowledge, competency and behaviours that are needed for customers. Skills for the team can be gained by:

- Recruiting new people with the required skills
- Redeploying people from one role to another within the team
- Training and developing people to improve their skills
- Coaching people to improve their skills on the job

To make sure that your team is effective for customers, it is essential for you to:

- Identify the Customer Based Skills that your team needs in order to achieve its objectives
- Identify the skills you have, and don't have, in the team
- Encourage individuals to measure their own customer-based skill levels
- Carry out a Team Skills Audit, to identify the gaps
- Match the skills of individuals to the work that needs to be done
- Plan in detail with team members the training, development and coaching activities that will produce the Customer Based Skills you need

Different Team Roles

Be aware of different team roles. Try to match the staff you have, their skills and attitudes, to the roles in the team. You will rarely achieve a perfect match, but try to have a systematic way of identifying your key skills gaps, and of linking these to the specific strengths and development needs of the individuals in the team.

BEST PRACTICE
Unicentro – Recruitment

James Wright-Smith, Senior Manager Planning and Research, Unicentro:
"Having the right people, in the right place, with the right level of skill, passion and commitment to the customer is the key to performance."

A Customer-Based Skills Inventory

Next you need to clarify exactly what skills you already have in your team. Encourage your team members to do this for themselves, by using the next activity.

WORK-BASED ACTIVITY

Customer Based Skills Requirements

What Customer Based Skills does your team need? Write a list of up to three main functions that your team is responsible for. Link each function to one or more Customer Based Skills. This will produce your Customer Based Skills requirements. An example has been included to start you off.

TEAM FUNCTIONS	CUSTOMER BASED SKILLS REQUIRED
1: Dealing with customers' telephone enquiries	Telephone skills Listening skills Giving information and advice Providing good product knowledge
2:	
3:	
4:	

Self Assessment – Your Customer Based Skills

Identify your own customer-based skills. Read the statements and think about your own level of confidence. Select the appropriate confidence level. You may also use this exercise for team members.

NAME OF TEAM MEMBER:
(if applicable)

JOB TITLE:

◉   Select to show whether you are **Very Confident**, **Could Improve** or **Not Confident** with this skill

CUSTOMER BASED SKILLS	Very Confident	Could Improve	Not Confident
Providing customer service within the rules (including legislation & organisational procedures)	O	O	O
Giving customers a positive impression of myself and my organisation	O	O	O
Deal with customers face to face	O	O	O
Deal with customers on the telephone	O	O	O
Promote additional services or products to customers	O	O	O
Recognise and deal with customer queries, requests and problems	O	O	O
Resolve customer service problems	O	O	O
Recognise diversity when delivering customer service	O	O	O
Support customer service improvements	O	O	O

Identify Your Key Issues from this Self Assessment:

(If you identify any customer based skills which a particular to your industry or sector, include them as well).

Seven Steps to Successful Coaching

1. Set ground rules – time, place, duration, frequency and process
2. Establish a rapport with the person being coached
3. Agree on goals and objectives – and link them to the customer related objectives for your organisation/team
4. Find the starting point
5. Devise an action plan
6. Gain the individual's commitment
7. Monitor the situation and provide feedback

4.5 Human Emotional Resources

Emotional Intelligence

When your team communicates with customers, encourage the use of emotional intelligence. In many instances, it is the emotional content of the service which makes it memorable to the customer. This could of course be either a favourable or an unfavourable memory! This emotional content can stimulate customers to become promoters, rather than mere participants in a transaction.

DEFINITION
Emotional Intelligence

Emotional Intelligence is the ability to understand your own emotions and those of your customers, and how they can change in different situations.

There is certainly an emotional side to the customer experience. The benefits to customers are that they are then working with people who are applying greater skills within the relationship. The people they are working with are able to do the following:

- Understand what is important to customers
- Empathise with customers
- Speak the customers' language
- Recognise the mood of the customer and react in a positive way

Encourage and equip your team to be aware of their own emotions and those of others, including internal and external customers. If you and your team are emotionally intelligent you will be better equipped to listen and deal with problems. For example, when giving constructive or developmental feedback to a team member, be aware that your own attitude, tone of voice and words will affect your team member's reaction. Equally, when dealing with a customer who is upset or angry, try not to simply reflect the customer's mood. Instead, think about how your own manner of communication – tone, words and body language – will affect the customer's emotional state. React and respond in the most emotionally intelligent way you can to enable the problem to be resolved.

Try not to simply reflect the customer's mood

Using Your Emotional Intelligence

Having an awareness of your own emotions and those of your customers is important. If you behave in an emotionally intelligent way you are better prepared to listen to customers, meet and exceed their expectations, and deal with any problems effectively. Even in teams with predominantly internal customers, the benefits of emotional intelligence are equally important - remember that the sum of your internal customer service will be reflected in the final level of service for the external customer.

The Six Competencies of Emotional Intelligence

Emotional Intelligence can be seen as the ability to know your feelings and use them to make good decisions. This can be broken down into the following activities of a person who is emotionally intelligent:

- Manage your feelings well
- Motivate yourself with zeal and persistence
- Maintain hope in the face of frustration
- Exhibit empathy and compassion
- Interact smoothly
- Manage relationships effectively

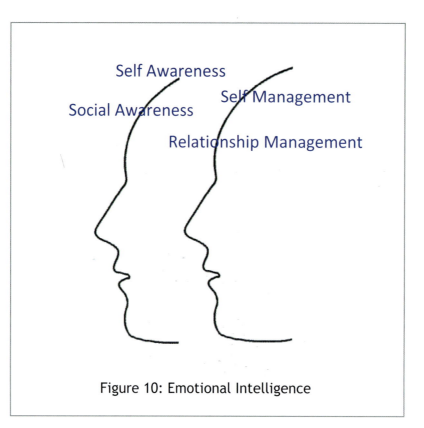

Figure 10: Emotional Intelligence

Manage Your Feelings

Be aware of your own emotions, your strengths and weaknesses, and of how you are likely to react in different situations with customers. Where difficult situations are encountered, you will be able to control your emotions, staying calm and devising an appropriate way to progress. For example, you are talking to a customer who appears angry or upset. You may recall from similar situations in the past that you are likely to respond by being defensive, and this would worsen the situation. Instead, make a conscious effort to stay calm and take the situation forward by finding out what the problem is. Stay in control of your own emotions to help, rather than exacerbate the problem.

Motivate Yourself with Zeal and Persistence

You work hard to understand your own motivating factors. You recognise what makes you tick. You have a determination to get the job done and to deal with any obstacles as best you can, without becoming quickly demoralised.

For example, you are facing a long, difficult task at work. It would be easy to become demoralised. Think about your own and your team's motivational factors—they could include giving oneself small rewards, taking short breaks from the task, perhaps breaking the task down into more manageable chunks. Or it could help to let colleagues know how hard you are finding it. Their interest and appreciation of your persistence may just be the spark that keeps you going.

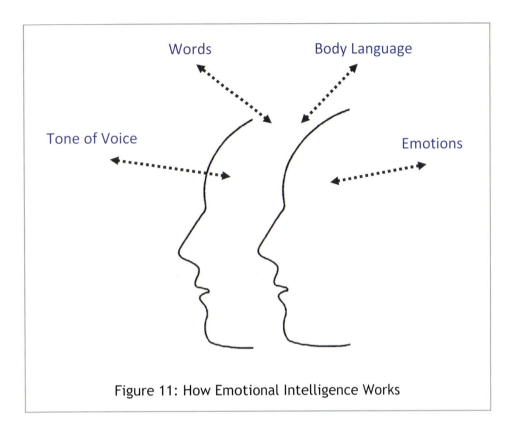

Figure 11: How Emotional Intelligence Works

Maintain Hope in the Face of Frustration

In difficult situations you are able to stay positive, and you recognise that this is important as a customer service ambassador. Frustrations, you realise, can be dealt with or minimised with a positive attitude.

As an example, you may be learning a new process at work. Things are not going well, and you could become demoralised and simply give up. This would not be for the best, though. Find out who can help you; are there any written guidelines or other documentation, or someone who has previously operated this process? Persist in the task, but in an intelligent and positive manner.

Exhibit Empathy and Compassion

Seeing things from the internal or external customer's or team member's point of view is essential. You are prepared to listen carefully, especially in difficult or uncomfortable situations. You use a wide range of listening methods.

If you are communicating with an internal customer who seems to have a problem, and they are simply not making sense, you could be tempted to be abrupt and move onto something else. Instead, take a few minutes to listen intelligently, and try to see what can be done to help. Ask questions sensitively to clarify the problem and gain a better understanding of it. Use your skills of empathy and compassion to help your internal customer - and set up a better relationship between the two of you, which could help you both in the future.

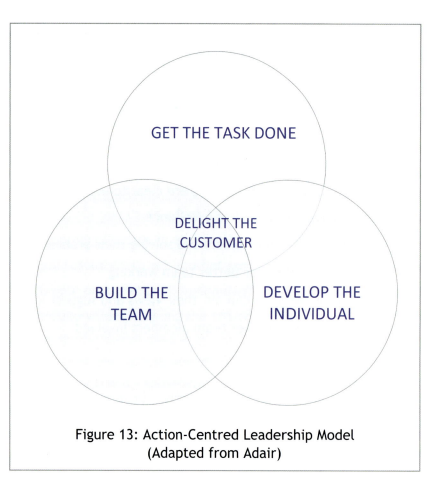

Figure 13: Action-Centred Leadership Model
(Adapted from Adair)

Task – Team – Individual

Think of "Task-Team-Individual" for your team tasks. In this activity, the first two items have been completed for you. Study these, then apply the same approach to the third item.

ITEM 1: **Planning an activity**

> **TASK:** Task clearly identified; Clear objectives; Priorities established; Resources allocated

> **TEAM:** Team involvement; Clear guidelines; Appropriate team size & structure; Appropriate mix of skills

> **INDIVIDUAL:** Agree responsibilities; Assess skills; Set performance targets; Agree support

ITEM 2: **Holding a meeting**

> **TASK:** Objectives of meeting are clear; Establish who attends; Location, seating, timings are set

> **TEAM:** How are actions recorded?; Discuss team performance and plans; Use the meeting to gel the team together; Consider possible conflict

> **INDIVIDUAL:** Encourage all to contribute; Listen to all points; Let people air their views..but do not let the meeting be hijacked

ITEM 3: (A task for your own team)

> **TASK:**

> **TEAM:**

> **INDIVIDUAL:**

4.9 Physical Resources

The physical resources that you need in your team – the buildings, office furniture, equipment, information and communications technology, protective clothing, and a host of other essentials for your day-to-day work – all support your team members in the delivery of their customer service. Ensure that both you and the team are aware of the organisation's processes for the acquisition and maintenance of these resources.

Think about how your physical resources assist in delivering excellent services for customers. With technology, and information technology in particular, it is often necessary to train your

Self Assessment - Team Culture

Complete this self assessment of your team's culture, to test the degree of customer focus you already have – and to identify the improvement actions needed. Don't forget to involve your team members in this self assessment – their perceptions are important, and are probably different from yours.

Select Yes or No	Yes	No
OUR CUSTOMER SERVICE STRATEGY:		
Our strategy is aligned to customers	O	O
We are committed to customers	O	O
LISTENING TO CUSTOMERS:		
We use a range of different listening methods	O	O
We capture customer feedback on a range of customer transactions and processes	O	O
WORKING WELL WITH PEOPLE:		
We communicate well	O	O
We value and respect our internal customers	O	O
CHANGE AND IMPROVEMENT:		
We are committed to continuous improvement	O	O
We innovate, to the benefit of customers	O	O

Identify Your Key Issues from this Self Assessment:

5.3 Team Communication

Effective Communications

Firstly, let us remind ourselves of the importance of communication. As organisations become more successful, they often grow - making team communication much more difficult. If we consider, for example, a family owned manufacturing business based in a single location, communication is much easier than in a global company with manufacturing sites in many countries. In the family owned business it is not unusual for the owner to know all the employees by name. The owner is also able to literally touch or challenge any interface with the customer very quickly. This can often help in the delivery of excellent service. In global companies, teams are often geographically spread out, with many more people involved and several layers of management, making effective team communication a much bigger challenge.

Teams are often geographically spread out .. making effective
team communication a much bigger challenge

Good communication is essential for the effectiveness of the team—and it has a major impact on customers, both internal and external. Think about the communications that take place:

- Between individual members of your team
- Between your team and other teams in the organisation - your internal customers
- Between your team and partner organisations, such as suppliers of raw materials and logistics providers
- Between your team and external customers

5.10 Team Action Plan and Progress Record

WORK-BASED ACTIVITY

Team Action Plan

Now you need to plan your areas for change.

- Write below the actions that you intend to take over the coming weeks and months

- Share the plans with your team to make sure they are all on board with the changes and improvements that you will lead

- Keep a check on your actions by reviewing them regularly at your team meetings

- Record the progress that you and your team make with your Team Action Plan

	ACTION	PROGRESS MADE/COMPLETED	DATE
1			
2			
3			
4			
5			

6   Dealing with Difficult Situations

Introduction

Welcome to Module 6. In this module we discuss the importance and methods of finding out about potential and actual customer service problems. Several ways of dealing with difficult customer service situations are described, and you could consider using some of these with your own team. Learning from customer service problems in order to improve service delivery is an essential part of the module.

6.1   Learning Outcomes

Learning Outcomes for Module 6

On successful completion of this module you should be able to:

- Understand how to listen to customers in order to identify potential and actual problems
- Identify the key steps to defusing potentially difficult situations
- Identify appropriate action to resolve customer service problems
- Understand the importance of learning from customer service problems

6.2   What Do I Need To Deal With?

Encourage your team to think about your customers' expectations of service. Most customers will anticipate that services will be delivered in a particular way to a specific standard or level. Just as with a product, when we buy something we expect it to be as advertised, of good quality and fit for purpose - "it does what it says on the tin." The same sorts of expectations apply to customer service. Recognition of your customers' expectations will prepare your team to deliver their services to an excellent level. Communicate this to your team, and reinforce the concept as often as you can.

Benefits of Resolving Customer Service Problems

If you think about it, there are some clear benefits of resolving customer service problems well. If you take the time and trouble to carefully manage difficult situations, the benefits are that:

- Complaining customers can turn out to be your most loyal ambassadors
- They will tell other people about your service recovery
- Your organisation will have increased customer retention and loyalty
- You will improve the professional image and reputation of your organisation

Customer Expectations

Levels of service experienced by customers could be anything from poor, through to average and good, to excellent. Customers are becoming more and more demanding. They now think of customer service in a similar way to a product. If your organisation's service does not meet their expectations, they defect to someone else - a competitor - who can meet the standards they want.

Even if you do not have direct competitors, which may be the case with a public service organisation, a charitable trust or passenger transport providers for example, disappointed and frustrated customers can cause your organisation to lose its contract, be penalised, or lose out in some other way. Therefore everything we say here applies to non-competitive organisations just as much as to competitive ones.

Service Delivery Gap

However one defines the level of service delivered to customers, you and your team need to match it against their expectations. Any gap between the two - the Service Delivery Gap - is a real problem for your team and organisation.

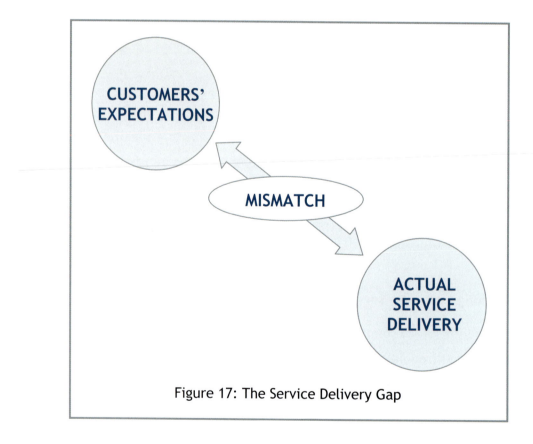

Figure 17: The Service Delivery Gap

The Service Delivery Gap could be caused by one of two factors:

- Your customers' expectations involve more than you can offer, or
- Your organisation's service processes have not been followed

Remember that customers' expectations often comprise a set of individual services. Take the example of a train journey. What are our expectations of that journey? Every individual customer is, of course, different; some will expect different products and services from others, but typically we might expect on a train journey:

- Helpful timetable information
- Efficient ticket purchasing
- The train arrives and leaves on time, and generally keeps to the timetable
- We have a safe and comfortable place to wait
- We experience a safe, clean, healthy and comfortable journey
- When we get on board, there is a seat available
- The staff are friendly, courteous, helpful, knowledgeable and efficient

If any of those individual services are missing or poorly delivered, then the whole purchase has not met the customer's expectations, and a potential problem has arisen. Hence your team needs to be both consistent in delivering the services, and be on the look-out for possible breakdowns in service delivery. This also demonstrates the critical importance of teamwork and communication – a typical customer is experiencing a number of individual services, from different people, at different times and in different places. Putting an effective Service Chain in place, with people working together and communicating well, will help to avoid and resolve any problems.

Being aware of precisely where things can go wrong will ensure that you and your team are better prepared to resolve problems well. Some possible causes of problems are:

- Your Service Promise has been broken
- The customer thinks you don't care
- You over-promise and under-deliver
- You have not kept the customer informed
- There has been poor communication regarding your product or service
- Unprofessional behaviour of one of your team
- Your organisation has handled a complaint badly

Transactional Analysis is one tool which is quite easy to understand and use in outline. At a simple level, using the principles of Transactional Analysis will give your team confidence and competence when dealing with a range of difficult interactions with customers – including handling conflicts and difficult people.

DEFINITION

Transactional Analysis

Transactional Analysis is a framework for describing behaviour in an interchange between two people. It can help in understanding why people react the way they do, especially when dealing with difficult customer service situations.

Ego States

Transactional Analysis identifies several Ego States which we may adopt when interacting with others – either unconsciously or consciously.

Adult   This is being spontaneous and aware, and reacting to the here and now. It is the preferred ego state.

Child   In this ego state we experience behaviours, thoughts, and feelings which are replayed from our own childhood.

Parent   In this ego state we adopt behaviours, thoughts and feelings which are copied from our parents.

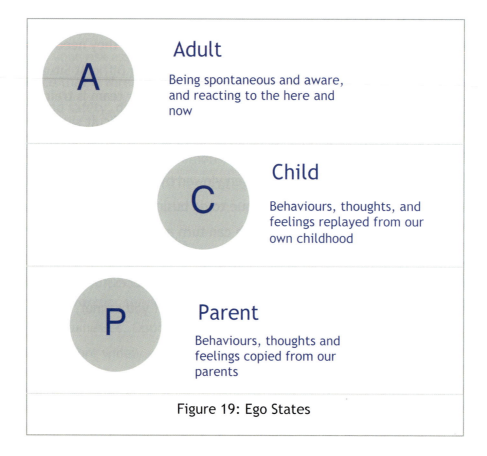

Adult

A

Being spontaneous and aware, and reacting to the here and now

Child

C

Behaviours, thoughts, and feelings replayed from our own childhood

Parent

P

Behaviours, thoughts and feelings copied from our parents

Figure 19: Ego States

Conversation Types

When you are conducting a conversation with a customer (whether external or internal), the Transactional Stimulus and the Transactional Response are key aspects.

DEFINITION

Transactional Stimulus and Transactional Response

The Transactional Stimulus is the initial message sent by one of the participants in an interaction between two people. The Transactional Stimulus could be one of the types: Adult, Child or Parent. This message or stimulus will normally be followed by a Transactional Response from the other person – which again could be either Adult, Child or Parent in type.

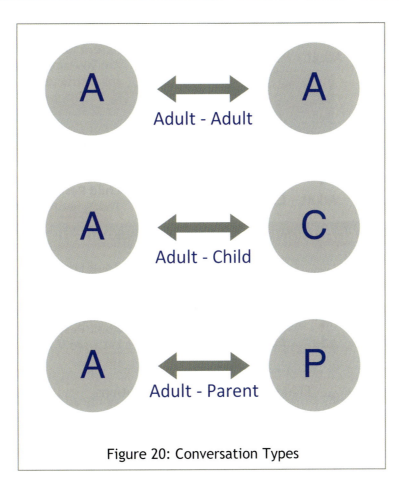

Figure 20: Conversation Types

Look for the Transactional Stimulus – and then respond in the best way to calm the situation and resolve the difficulty, by adopting an Adult Ego State.

- Stating what you want, think and feel
- Standing up for what you believe to be correct
- Listening to the other person and acknowledging their views
- Relaxed body posture and facial expression
- Being open and honest with the other person

Aggressive Behaviour

This is when you disregard the feelings and views of others. You put your own wants before those of other people, and signs of aggressive behaviour are quite easy to spot. They include:

- Speaking loudly or shouting
- Giving orders
- Finger wagging and pointing
- Interrupting others
- Putting others down
- Using sarcasm

The best behaviour for your team members to use as Customer Service Professionals is assertive behaviour. It is not always easy, because they (and you) may have to deal with customers who act aggressively. So here are some tips to help when dealing with aggressive people:

- Be confident in your voice, facial expression and posture - if your body language is assertive your mind will probably soon follow
- Ask appropriate questions which will defuse the situation
- Be factual – don't be tempted to always express your own opinions or emotions
- Work out how the situation can be taken forward and state clearly and calmly what you intend to do
- Maintain eye contact with your customers but do not glare
- If it helps and it is appropriate, apologise. However, do not simply admit blame on behalf of your organisation or other people just to satisfy an aggressive customer - in other words, don't be submissive
- If the aggression of the customer goes beyond your ability to handle the situation, know when to escalate the problem to your line manager – this is a key part of the process which you must find out about as a matter of priority
- At all times act professionally and calmly

The Belief Cycle

Let's look at the Belief Cycle – it's a simple concept that can help you to deal with a difficult customer service situation.

166

By acting in an emotionally intelligent way, you focus on your own feelings and behaviours when you are dealing with a difficult situation. This is really useful when you have to interact with someone who is angry or upset. It does happen from time to time, whether it is internal or external customers that you are dealing with. It may even be that you have an aggressive person to deal with, so use the Belief Cycle to understand what is happening and prepare yourself for this type of interaction.

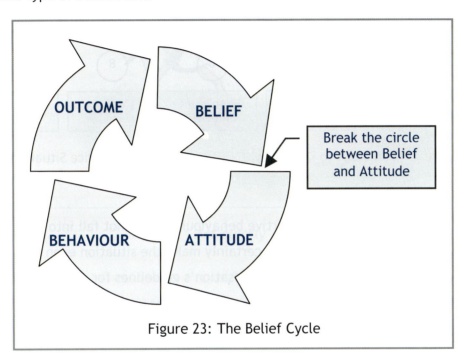

Figure 23: The Belief Cycle

The Belief Cycle can act as a vicious circle and, unchecked, can actually worsen interactions with customers who are proving challenging already.

This is how it works:

- If your belief is simply that the customer is being rude, perhaps with no good reason, your feelings may turn to anger.

- If you are angry this tends to make your own behaviour aggressive.

- The outcome is that the interaction will degenerate further, and so the problem becomes worse.

The way to deal with the Belief Cycle when it is working against you is to break the circle between Belief and Attitude. Whatever the reason for the customer's aggressive behaviour, use your Emotional Intelligence to change your own feelings from anger to assertiveness.

- Use Emotional Intelligence to change your own attitude

- Change your own mode of behaviour from anger to assertiveness

- In that way, the outcome becomes a much more manageable and calmer interaction

Ensure you have well thought-out and reliable procedures for dealing with problems and complaints. Treat complaints "as a gift." Dealt with in the right way they will help you to improve rapidly. The old-fashioned approach of brushing complaints under the carpet, and concepts such as "we have never had a complaint" should be replaced by a healthy, open attitude to service recovery.

Encourage in your team full discussion of customers' problems and complaints. Adopt a no-blame culture to ensure that problems are identified quickly, before they reach a more serious stage. Complaints can actually be good for an organisation because:

- They enable customers to have their problems solved quickly and effectively
- Customers whose problems have been dealt with well can become loyal ambassadors
- Complaints are critical to identifying and implementing improvements in your services – they are "free customer feedback"

174

Now think about your own team and organisation – and whether your procedures for service recovery are truly effective.

WORK-BASED ACTIVITY
Review Your Complaints Policy and Practice

Write a brief summary of how complaints are handled in your team and/or your organisation. Include internal complaints as well as those from external customers. Try to identify three clear, practical steps you could take in your team to improve your team and/or your organisation's policy and practice in handling and resolving complaints.

How complaints are handled:

Three steps to improve your complaint resolution:

1

2

3

Service Recovery - Dos and Don'ts

DO:

- Welcome complaints – they help you to improve
- Regularly review complaints with your team to ensure nothing is missed
- Learn from complaints – make changes to your procedures to remove the underlying causes of problems
- Publish a clear and workable complaints procedure
- Communicate with customers so that they know how their problem is being dealt with
- Find ways to capture compliments as well as complaints

DON'T:

- Brush complaints under the carpet
- Blame people for causing problems – just focus on how to improve
- See complaints as a sign of weakness or failure – customers understand that things sometimes go wrong, but they want to deal with an organisation that sorts things out as quickly as possible
- Forget to include checkpoints in your service recovery process, so that somebody (perhaps you as the Manager or Team Leader) is routinely monitoring progress towards service recovery

The Plan - Deliver - Follow-up Routine

In your team, incorporate the routine of Plan - Deliver - Follow-Up into transactions with customers. Most transactions should include the three steps. Try including this routine approach to customer service transactions in your employee induction programme for new team members and reinforce it within your learning and development activities.

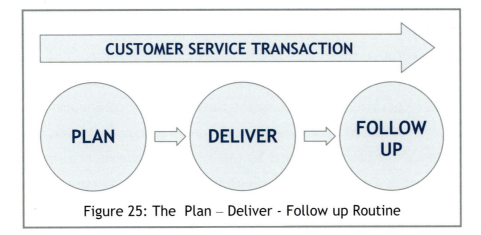

Figure 25: The Plan – Deliver - Follow up Routine

- **Plan:** Think now about how you and your team will deliver your customer service before you even see your customers. What do you need to do? What information will you need? Will you need to involve your colleagues and do you know if they are available? Do you know how to use the correct procedure?

- **Deliver:** When you deliver customer service, try to get it right, first time, every time. For a customer this could be your one opportunity to get it right. If you have the right skills, information and support you can delight your customer and begin to build a long term customer relationship.

- **Follow-up:** Always follow up the delivery of customer service. You need to find out what went well and what can be improved. Think carefully about how you follow up your service delivery.

DEFINITION
Continuous Improvement

Continuous improvement is the ongoing search, throughout an organisation, for better ways of working that will increase the level of quality of products and services.

BEST PRACTICE
Euro-Deporte – Continuous Improvement

James Wright-Smith, Senior Manager Planning and Research, Unicentro:

"In our company continuous improvement must not be driven by initiatives - it should result from our whole, embedded customer focused culture; having an obsession with customer satisfaction; forever looking to change processes because there is always a better way of doing things to be found. Managers must empower all staff to stimulate process improvement."

Learning from Problems

Sometimes, when a customer begins dealing with a customer service department, for example, he or she is already in a negative mindset. The best customer service representatives are not those that simply neutralise the problem. Outstanding customer service representatives take a negative and turn it into a positive. That ensures the customer is not only happy, but is convinced that he or she has had an outstanding experience - the organisation has gone the extra mile. It can often be the process that has let the customer down, so ensure you give feedback to your manager, and don't be afraid of offering a solution. You work with the process daily, so you are the one who often knows what the problems are and how to overcome them – don't keep it to yourself! It is often the case that processes need to be improved in order to avoid or reduce customer service problems. An organisation that practices Continuous Improvement uses feedback from customers and staff to improve the effectiveness of its processes.

6.7   End-of-Module Knowledge-Check

KNOWLEDGE-CHECK 6.3

⊙   Select the best answer to the question:

1   When using the Belief Cycle for guidance in handling a conversation with an angry customer, the main aim should be to:

    A ○ Break the circle between Belief and Attitude

    B ○ Break the circle between Outcome and Results

    C ○ Break the circle between Attitude and Outcome

2   Because customers are generally becoming more demanding, if their expectations are not met they are likely to:

    A ○ Purchase at a lower price

    B ○ Defect to a competitor

    C ○ Remain loyal in spite of any problems

3   The Service Delivery Gap is the difference between:

    A ○ Customers' expectations and actual service delivery

    B ○ The times of purchase and delivery

    C ○ The making of a complaint and the organisation's Service Recovery

4   A useful guide-line when resolving customer service problems is described by the phrase:

    A ○ Respond - Resolve - Improve

    B ○ Plan - Resolve - Improve

    C ○ Plan - Resolve - Communicate

5   Your team's effective resolution of customer service problems benefits:

    A ○ Mainly Customers

    B ○ Customers, Managers and Team Members

    C ○ Mainly Managers

6.8   Team Action Plan and Progress Record

Team Action Plan

Now you need to plan your areas for change.

- Write below the actions that you intend to take over the coming weeks and months

- Share the plans with your team to make sure they are all on board with the changes and improvements that you will lead

- Keep a check on your actions by reviewing them regularly at your team meetings

- Record the progress that you and your team make with your Team Action Plan

	ACTION	PROGRESS MADE/COMPLETED	DATE
1			
2			
3			
4			
5			

7 Making it Happen

Introduction

Welcome to Module 7. In this module we focus on change in organisations, and the practical steps that a Manager or Team Leader should consider in order to implement the improvements needed for excellent customer service. Some typical Barriers to Change are identified, and you will be able to plan how to overcome them. Politics, in particular, is important in ensuring effective change implementation. Service partnerships are also reviewed as an important factor in moving towards service excellence.

7.1 Learning Outcomes

Learning Outcomes for Module 7

On successful completion of this module you should be able to:

- Identify the main features of change in an organisation

- Identify typical Barriers to Change

- Understand key tactics to assist a Manager or Team Leader in achieving desired changes

- Show an understanding of the importance of Service Partnerships in a team delivering excellent customer service

7.2 Doesn't It Happen Anyway?

Make it Happen

Change and innovation are permanent features of modern businesses. Customers' expectations are continually changing, and your organisation, including your own team, needs to respond to them. Many of today's organisations recognise the importance of their customers. They understand that they need to establish a reputation for excellent service – it is the differentiator in a competitive marketplace. However, even those organisations that have the right Customer Service Strategies in place may fail to achieve the levels of service that they are looking for. Their key to success is in being able to implement their strategy – in other words, to make it happen.

As a Manager or Team Leader of customer service, this may be your one, key responsibility – to ensure that the strategy, aims, objectives, policies and processes for customer service are put into place throughout your team so that your customers experience the very best service. Of course, the end result can only really be judged by the customers themselves, and not by how good your internal processes are. No matter how effective and customer focused the organisation's internal structures and policies are, unless the experience of the customer is a positive one, you will not have achieved your goal of service excellence.

So focus your efforts on making it happen. Think carefully about your plans and objectives for your team, and use all the resources available to you to implement the Customer Focused Culture in your team.

Change

Change can sometimes be difficult to achieve in teams. There may be obstacles that stand in the way of change, even if it clearly needs to happen. For each change that you are planning, think through and discuss with your team the process of making the change. Where there are objections, tackle them with open, calm rational arguments, giving reasons for the change, and painting a picture of the improvements that the change will bring about. Get your people on board - without them, change simply won't happen.

WORK-BASED ACTIVITY

Changing the Culture

Think about your own team. Recall the changes that you have already identified and planned. Select three of them as priority changes that you will implement in your team - in order to create or enhance a Customer Focused Culture. Now convert these three priority changes into SMART actions for yourself – stating specifically what will you do, and when, in order to make the changes happen.

SMART ACTIONS	DATE
Action 1	
Action 2	
Action 3	

7.3 Continuous Change

Preparing for Change

As a Manager or Team Leader it is part of your responsibility to look out for changes that are needed, and then to help implement them. Of course, changes are often difficult to work through. Some changes might have a major impact on the way people work, and so some of your team members can feel uncomfortable, or even threatened. Change, though, is a fact of life. Help your team as a whole, and the individuals within it, to work with the changes that are needed in order to drive towards customer service excellence.

Some typical reasons for change can be:

- Changes in technology

- Changes in customer tastes and expectations

- Business changes brought about through competition, mergers and takeovers

- Global changes

- The need for improvements, identified through Complaint Analysis, for example

- Structural changes in an organisation

Making the Changes

For some it is a natural reaction at work to resist change, unless it is managed well. This is true even when the change will benefit the person as well as the organisation. As the Manager or Team Leader, do not be afraid of change. Every organisation will go through change; however, change can cause upset and threat. Welcome the opportunity to improve the way you and your team do things. Focus on how change can improve your customer service – and how that will be good for business, and good for you as an individual.

As the Manager or Team Leader, do not be afraid of change

The way you bring in changes is the key to success or failure. If you do it effectively, change has the power to motivate your team, rather than de-motivate. The basic principle is to be open in discussing fully the need for changes, and then to plan, with your team, how to implement them. Empower your team to bring in the changes and seek their input and ideas on how to make them happen.

Managing Change Dos and Don'ts

DO:

- Openly discuss why changes are needed
- Allow time for group discussions and individual one-to-ones
- Plan in detail how changes will be brought in.
- Review and evaluate, with your team, as you go through the change process.
- Look for an ally who will support you if most of your team are against the changes
- Communicate, communicate, communicate – to avoid the "rumour-machine" taking over!

DON'T:

- Impose changes without discussion.
- Instruct or deliver a monologue when explaining changes.
- Ignore the fears and hopes of your team members.
- Be put off by your team's fears – some changes are essential, even if nobody seems to want them

Unicentro – Making Changes

Stephanie Osario, one of Unicentro's managers, wants to set up a computer-based logging system to ensure that all comments, compliments and complaints from customers are captured and dealt with as customer feedback. This is a change from the existing process, which is to record complaints, but no other customer feedback, in a book kept in the Customer Services kiosk.

Some Unicentro employees in the centre are opposed to this change – they think it would waste too much time, having to enter every comment into a computer terminal. Stephanie is considering how to implement this new process. Which is Stephanie's best course of action?

◉   Select the best answer to the question:

A O   Hold a meeting to explain the change and allow discussion on its pros and cons

B O   Hold a meeting and let the centre staff vote on the change

C O   Implement the change straight away and do not waste time on discussion

7.4   Removing the Barriers

Remove all the Barriers To Change preventing you and your team from achieving the changes that are vital for delivering excellent customer service.

- Identify each Barrier to Change in turn
- Analyse the Barrier to Change – is it a department, a person/people, a process or a cultural issue?
- Plan how to dismantle the Barrier to Change
- Use politics (referring to the next section for details) to help you
- Discuss all the key issues with your team, so that they are engaged in helping to achieve the changes
- Regularly review your progress
- Be prepared to modify your plans in order to meet changing circumstances and new barriers

7.5   Recognising and Using Politics

Politics

People influence how the organisation does its work. No matter what policies, procedures, processes and structures exist in an organisation, politics are important to what actually takes place. Politics in this context concerns the internal relationships and power structures that exist, in addition to, and sometimes in contrast to the organisation's official structures and policies.

Politics should be recognised by any Manager or Team Leader – and you can make good use of these informal relationships to help push through the changes that are so important for your Customer Focused Culture. Use the following guide-line to help.

Using Politics when Implementing Change

- Try to get to know who holds power and influence in your area of the organisation

- Build good working relationships with the people who can either help or hinder with changes

- Communicate effectively with the right people, using appropriate methods, whether formal or informal

- Don't underestimate the power of unofficial communication channels, such as the "rumour mill" and gossip – these, again, can either help or hinder your changes

- Be open in your communications; don't be tempted to push any change through without talking it through with the appropriate people, both inside and outside your team

- Sometimes you will need to make changes which others do not agree with – let them know what will happen, with reasons, but be prepared to do things which some people are not going to like

- When you come across an objector who holds considerable influence, engage the support of others in order to overcome the objections

Know who holds power and influence

7.6   Using Service Partnerships

To maintain and build on relationships with your customers – both internal and external – your team needs to deliver consistent and reliable customer service. In addition, customers want to feel that you are making every possible effort to meet and exceed their expectations. This builds customer loyalty from external customers and longer-term Service Partnerships with internal customers.

Set the best example to your team members by being proactive in your dealings with your customers, trying to anticipate their expectations and understanding how a successful Service Partnership can move their business forward as well as your own, especially in a B2B situation. You will sometimes need to negotiate between your customers and your organisation or department in order to find the best way of meeting your customers' expectations. In addition you will need to make extra efforts to delight your customers by giving higher levels of service than they expect.

Excellent customer service relies on teamwork. As the Manager or Team Leader, part of your responsibility is to manage and coordinate your Service Chain. In many situations, successful delivery of service to external customers relies on a complete and effective Service Chain of internal customers and internal or external suppliers. The Service Chain needs to effectively link a number of people, departments, contractors or suppliers, each of whom delivers a different element of the total service that the customer requires. The customer's experience depends upon the ability of the organisation to manage its Service Chain effectively.

A well-managed Service Chain will deliver a high level of service for customers. In contrast, a poorly managed Service Chain has a negative impact upon customers – they may, for example, experience delays or gain the feeling of being "passed from pillar to post" as the organisation struggles to deliver the seamless service that the customer is looking for. In short, an ineffectively managed Service Chain means that your customers do not find you "easy to do business with."

For example, in the passenger transport industry, a poorly managed Service Chain could, for a rail passenger, be caused by the railway company failing to control its maintenance and cleaning operations. The impact on the customer will be delays, late trains, dirty carriages and breakdowns. If the railway company manages the Service Chain well, these different elements within its Service Chain will integrate well and provide a seamless service to both external and internal customers. For this to work, a series of Service Partnerships must be formed which will enable the chain to work efficiently and effectively.

The Service Offer and the Service Chain

Effective organisations frequently review their Service Offer. This is important in order to continue to meet and exceed the rising expectations of customers, and also to keep ahead of competitors in a commercial market. In public sector, non-competitive organisations too, the Service Offer is an important aspect of service excellence; the Service Offer can be benchmarked against other organisations in order to ensure everything is being done to maximise customer satisfaction.

A new Service Offer must be properly designed and planned, because it will generally require changes in the service chain. Different service partners may need to be involved where new service characteristics are being delivered

Think carefully as the Manager or Team Leader about your own Service Offer, and how you need to work effectively within the Service Chain, developing the links that cement key relationships. Effective communication and an understanding of the roles of different organisations, departments and individuals are central to this area of your work.

KNOWLEDGE-CHECK 7.2

GCU Finance – Implementing a New Online Banking System

GCU Finance believes that "innovation for customers is the lifeblood of GCU" to quote from its Mission Statement. True to this principle, it is making a major revision to its online banking system for personal and business account holders. Due to the changes in the way the system works, the Service Chains which exist will need to be re-designed.

Jean Dupree, who is in charge of Online Customer Services, has been asked by one of his team, "What actually is a Service Chain?" Three other team members try to explain what it means. Which explanation is the closest to the correct meaning?

⊙   Select the best answer to the question:

A ○   Service Chains are boundaries which ensure we don't lose customers to our competitors

B ○   Service Chains in GCU are about responding to customer enquiries as fast as possible

C ○   A Service Chain links together the people in GCU who are needed to provide Seamless Service to customers

Costs and Benefits of Service Partnerships

Assess the costs and benefits to your customer and your organisation of any agreement that you make with your customers and partners – especially if it falls outside of the normal process that your organisation operates. Be clear, during the negotiation, that what is being suggested is beneficial to all sides, keeping in mind the concept of Win-Win. The partnership is all about working for both you and your partner, so being clear on costs and benefits will allow you to make the right decision, using, if appropriate, the advice of your own manager when you are in any doubt at all.

WORK-BASED ACTIVITY

Self Assessment - Making it Happen

Complete this self assessment of your team's readiness for change. Don't forget to involve your colleagues and team members in this self assessment if possible.

◉ Select Yes or No	Yes	No
CHANGE:		
The team is positive about changes in the way things are done	○	○
Changes are often suggested by team members, and then discussed and either implemented or rejected	○	○
POLITICS:		
I am knowledgeable about the informal relationships and power structures in the organisation	○	○
I am confident in using politics to help push through changes	○	○
PARTNERSHIPS:		
My team understands the service partnerships that are needed to give seamless service to customers	○	○
I am skilled in negotiating with others to build service partnerships in the interest of customers	○	○

Identify Your Key Issues from this Self Assessment:

7.7 End-of-Module Knowledge-Check

KNOWLEDGE-CHECK 7.3

◉ Select the best answer to the question:

1 Which is the most accurate description of most modern businesses in relation to Change?

    A O Change and Innovation are permanent features of modern businesses

    B O Change and Innovation are occasional features of modern businesses

    C O Change and Innovation are mainly a feature of new businesses

2 In order to successfully implement Change in a team, the required changes should be:

    A O Brought in as quickly as possible without the need for discussion

    B O Put off until the whole team agrees with them

    C O Discussed fully, identifying the reasons and benefits of changes

3 When a Manager who is trying to make changes comes across an objector who holds considerable influence, a useful approach is to:

    A O Engage the support of others in order to overcome the objections

    B O Engage the support of customers in order to overcome the objections

    C O Treat the objections as unimportant

4 Service Partnerships with internal customers can be important for some teams, because they are needed to:

    A O Deliver excellent service to external customers

    B O Satisfy the demands of team members

    C O Undercut the prices of competitors

5 A poorly managed Service Chain would normally have:

    A O Most impact on internal customers

    B O A positive effect on external customer service

    C O A negative effect on external customer service

7.8   Team Action Plan and Progress Record

Team Action Plan

Now you need to plan your areas for change.

- Write below the actions that you intend to take over the coming weeks and months
- Share the plans with your team to make sure they are all on board with the changes and improvements that you will lead
- Keep a check on your actions by reviewing them regularly at your team meetings
- Record the progress that you and your team make with your Team Action Plan

	ACTION	PROGRESS MADE/COMPLETED	DATE
1			
2			
3			
4			
5			

8   Embedding Innovation in Your Team

Introduction

Welcome to Module 8. In this module we will consider the role of innovation in the delivery of excellent customer service, and how this can be achieved within your team. Keeping to the rules and guide-lines are important when delivering and improving customer service processes. Technology will also be discussed, from the point of view of improving services for customers.

8.1   Learning Outcomes

Learning Outcomes for Module 8
On successful completion of this module you should be able to: • Understand the role of innovation in helping a team to deliver excellent customer service • Recognise the importance of keeping to the rules when improving customer service • Understand how technology may be used to improve service for customers

8.2   What is Innovation?

Innovation for customers is important for you, your team and your organisation. With customers becoming ever more demanding in their expectations of products and services, you should include innovation (in its many forms) as a key part of your team culture. Innovation is not just about introducing changes in your Core Products and Services, nor does it only concern changes in technology. Innovation also includes developing new ways of doing things – such as improving your processes, finding better ways of communicating with customers, and making complaint handling more effective. Innovation should be seen as any change which has a positive effect on your customer service.

The innovations you choose to implement must be properly planned and agreed, and must also be worthwhile from a business point of view. You could bring in some new technology which your customers thought was absolutely wonderful, but if it costs your organisation more than the benefits it generates then it is not something that you will choose to do.

Many forms of innovation, however, can be simple, cheap and easy to implement. To take advantage of these opportunities to innovate, your team needs a culture of innovation. When your team members are always on the look-out for new ways of improving service, finding stunning new methods of delighting your customers (perhaps before anyone else in your sector has thought of them), then you can be sure that your team has a Customer Focused Culture. The nature of customer service means that innovation, in all sorts of forms, is essential for service excellence.

The forms of innovation that you adopt in your team could be any of the following:

- Developing new processes which work better for customers

- Using new technology in a way which benefits your external customers

- Using new technology in a way which benefits your internal customers

- Enabling your customers to learn to use your technology

- Developing new products and services for customers

- Designing better organisational and team structures which empower your people to deliver excellent customer service

- Providing a wider range of communication methods, so that customers with different preferences can choose the method that suits them individually

Innovating for customers

192

Self Assessment - Innovation

Complete this self assessment of how effectively your team innovates for customers. Remember to consider your internal customers. If possible, involve your team members in this self assessment.

◉ Select Yes or No	Yes	No
IMPROVING PROCESSES:		
We use problems and breakdowns in services to improve processes	○	○
Our team has a culture of continuous improvement	○	○
EMPOWERING TEAM MEMBERS:		
Team members are encouraged to suggest better ways of doing things	○	○
Team members are empowered to deal with problems themselves	○	○
INNOVATING FOR CUSTOMERS:		
We design processes around customers	○	○
We use technology changes to make things better for customers	○	○

Identify Your Key Issues from this Self Assessment:

8.3   Using Customer Service as a Competitive Tool

Establish a competitive spirit in your team around innovation. The more ideas your team members generate, the better the chances of finding the innovations which will put you ahead of the competition. Even if you work in a non-competitive environment, perhaps a health service or local government organisation, the spirit of healthy competition within the team will drive forward the customer focused culture. Even non-competitive organisations have to satisfy, impress and delight their customers – sometimes in order to maintain contracts or to gain positive approval from regulatory bodies. So, whatever type of organisation you are in, discover an appropriate way of building the principle of "innovation for competitiveness" into your team.

When you are thinking of introducing innovations and improvements, consider the following three aspects:

1. How the improvements increase customer satisfaction
2. To what extent the improvements are affordable and achievable within your team's current constraints (for example finances and human resources)
3. Whether potential improvements conflict in any way with organisational and legal requirements

8.4 Empower to Innovate

To innovate successfully it is necessary to empower your team members. If they are empowered they have a fuller picture of what makes a Seamless Service for customers. Empowered employees are better motivated, and they will deliver the new ideas and processes that you are looking for. An empowered team member is able to see the whole impact of a suggested improvement, and can take you through the effects any change will have on other processes. In contrast, a team member who is not empowered, and hence only sees processes from a narrow viewpoint, will discover fewer effective changes that will really work for customers.

KNOWLEDGE-CHECK 8.1

Innovating for Your Customers

At Euro-Deporte you are trying to establish a customer focused culture in the team at all the company's fitness centres. As part of the culture you have realised that there is a need to motivate staff at the centres to invent new ideas, especially those which refresh customer service – this will attract and retain customers, and increase efficiency. Customers need a constant flow of new fitness offers - products, initiatives, events, promotions, equipment, fitness classes and techniques, in order to be attracted to, and stay with the centre.

Some innovations are delivered from Euro-Deporte's head office – the Marketing and Product Development Unit, which sets the overall direction of the company, and implements the major changes throughout the company. However the centres, you believe, should be more proactive in developing their own, centre-based innovations. You are considering how best to achieve this. Which is your best approach to innovation at the fitness centres?

◉   Select the best answer to the question:

A ○   Design new offers at Head Office, and rely on each Centre Manager to implement them

B ○   Engage customers in the innovation process by inviting them to centre-based focus groups and asking them what they would like to see

C ○   Engage staff in the innovation process by requiring them all to think up at least one innovation per month, to be included in their performance targets

8.5 Using Technology to Improve Services for Customers

Using Technology to Support Customers

Part of innovation is using technology, which should be used in order to support customers. Today's customers are becoming used to technology – at least some of them are. Make certain that your team's use of technology for customers is aligned with the skills that your customers actually have. Technology can be great for customers – and great for the team. However, technology sometimes gets in the way of excellent service. Instead of being used to support customer service, technology is too often used to help the organisation solve a problem in the short term – to the detriment of customers! Make sure this does not happen in your team.

Customers Demand the Best of Both Worlds

Customers want to be able to use efficient technological solutions – like E-Commerce and web-based order tracking – but they want help and a Personal Touch when they need it as well. While the 24-hour society, enabling customers to access services on a non-stop basis is good for business, it also creates pressures on the business and perhaps on your own team.

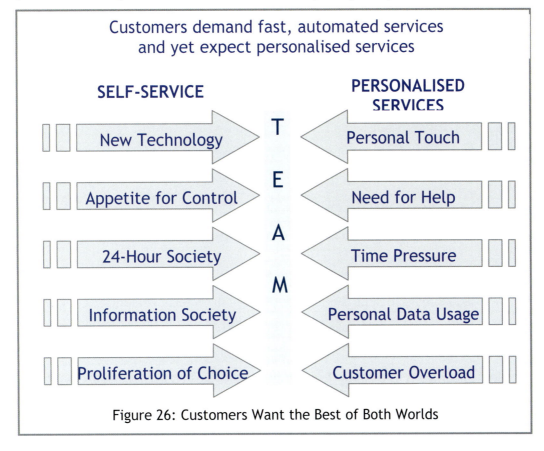

Figure 26: Customers Want the Best of Both Worlds

Looking at Figure 26, you can see that the increasing expectations of service - both automated and yet personal as well - can create pressures on your team. Your team (depending on the sector you are working in) may need to deliver "self-service" effectively, shown on the left of the diagram, and yet provide the personalised items on the right as well in order to give customers the personal dimension that they are looking for.

Good News, Bad News

Look at some views of customers in the Good News and Bad News for using technology. They show how technology can work both for and against the customer.

GUIDE-LINE
Technology – Good News and Bad News

THE GOOD NEWS:

- "Online shopping is easy, handy and efficient. It helps us, as we have no car."

- "The scanning tills are so much quicker and the receipt has more information."

- "I ordered books on the Internet; two days later the books arrived exactly when they said they would."

- "Booking flights is easy and efficient. I got a ticket and collected it at the airport from a machine."

THE BAD NEWS:

- "I ordered a new SIM card but when it arrived I couldn't activate it. I called the company but the first two operators couldn't help. The third managed to help - eventually."

- "I phoned a call centre and had to wait 20 minutes to be dealt with. It was a premium rate line - I think they make us wait to charge us more."

- "There is far too much automation; it gets really confusing, sometimes you just give up."

Ensure that technology is used to help rather than hinder. If you change your processes, or introduce a new technology, look at the impact on the customer. Telephone contact centres are an example of this. In the best cases a contact centre is really helpful – and makes the organisation easy to do business with. In the worst cases – and most of us have experienced them – the contact centre is extremely frustrating, and drives customers away to other organisations where they will be better treated.

Help Customers Learn to Use Your Technology

You may need to help your customers learn how to use your new technology effectively. E-Commerce is a good example. Customers are buying goods online more and more – and the most customer focused organisations think carefully about the skills and experiences that different customers have in using web-based systems. While some customer are web-competent, others are less sure, and a bad experience in trying but failing to use a new web-based e-commerce system could put them off dealing with your organisation.

If your team is going to do more business with customers through websites, make sure that:

- The customer impact of the change is seriously considered

- The design of the web-based system focuses on customers and their varying skills levels

- There is sufficient opportunity and information for customers to learn how to use the system

- There is effective help for customers who have a problem with using the new technology

In the worst cases .. the contact centre is extremely frustrating

To help you make the best use of technology in your team and your organisation, use the following guide-line.

GUIDE-LINE
Technology Action List for Managers and Team Leaders

- Resist the temptation to move over to new technology faster than the rate at which you can support the development of your customers
- Be customer-driven not technology-driven
- Use technology to enhance your offer - not to replace it
- Deploy technology to add value for the customer
- Allow your customer to choose when to use technology; imposing it is dangerous strategy
- Don't use technology to find solutions to problems that don't exist
- Develop your team members (the internal customers) and give them the tools and capability to be competent
- Base your decisions on sound research; don't guess what your customers want - find out!

Using Technology to Improve Services for Customers

Technology can affect your customers – in both positive and negative ways. Consider some technological changes that you could introduce – and how they will affect your customers. Think of two positive actions that you can take in your own team that will improve services for customers. (An example has been given for you). Identify both the benefits and the threats for your customers of each action.

EXAMPLE POSITIVE ACTION:	Website re-design
Current situation:	Our competitors are increasing sales through their websites
Positive action:	We will re-design our website, enabling customers to purchase goods
Benefits for Customers:	Easier ordering, order any time of day, track order status
Threats for Customers:	Loss of customers through a hard-to-learn system New system takes time to work correctly

YOUR 1st POSITIVE ACTION:

Current situation:

Positive action:

Benefits for Customers:

Threats for Customers:

YOUR 2nd POSITIVE ACTION:

Current situation:

Positive action:

Benefits for Customers:

Threats for Customers:

8.6   Improving Customer Service Within the Rules

Clearly, innovation and improvement needs to take place on a regular and systematic basis in order to keep up with the ever increasing demands of today's customers, and also in order for an organisation to stay ahead of its competitors. Your team and your organisation should have clear guide-lines for making changes and improvement – make certain that your team knows them, keeps to them, and even challenges them if they are standing in the way of improving the Customer's Experience.

To improve your customer service within the rules (of your organisation and your sector), adopt the following guide-lines.

GUIDE-LINE
Improving Customer Service Within the Rules

- Check the impact of your organisation's policies and procedures on proposed improvements or developments to customer service

- Obtain authorisation to change customer service practices

- Explain to the team the limits of their own authority, and who else needs to be involved for additional authority

- Explain to the team when and how to involve colleagues or service partners in the implementation of improvements or changes

- Explain relevant regulation and legislation relating to consumer protection

- Consider regulations relating to disability discrimination, equal opportunities, diversity and inclusion

- Look a the impact of changes on the health and safety of customers and colleagues

- Make certain that you as Manager or Team leader balance the requirements of regulation against the needs and objectives of your organisation and team

Business Case for Changes

You may need to prepare and present a Business Case when introducing changes and improvement in customer service. Do your research – consider all the options, and evaluate their respective benefits. Use Cost Benefit Analysis where possible, so that the full implications of changes are clearly stated in your Business Case. Do not forget to consider the effects of changes on your internal customers – on other units and departments, whose processes may also need to change as a result of what you propose.

8.7   End-of-Module Knowledge-Check

KNOWLEDGE-CHECK 8.2

◉   Select the best answer to the question:

1   Innovating effectively for customers can involve:

A O Introducing changes in processes only

B O Introducing changes in services only

C O Introducing changes in products, processes and services

2   When considering innovation, a key advantage of empowering team members is that:

A O Empowered team members can often see the impacts that any change will have on other processes

B O Empowered team members are more likely to keep to changed processes

C O Empowered team members are more likely to record new processes correctly

3   Helping customers to learn how to use any new technology that you introduce should be seen as:

A O A high-cost luxury

B O The customer's responsibility

C O An essential part of the change

4   When making changes and improvements in a team, it is very important to:

A O Check the impact that any changes will have on policies, procedures and guidelines

B O Check the impact of any changes on changes in other teams

C O Implement only a few changes over a period of time

5   The Health and Safety of customers and colleagues:

A O Is something that should be considered as a possible change impact

B O Is not likely to be affected by proposed changes

C O Is of minor importance when considering change impact

8.8   Team Action Plan and Progress Record

Team Action Plan

Now you need to plan your areas for change.

- Write below the actions that you intend to take over the coming weeks and months
- Share the plans with your team to make sure they are all on board with the changes and improvements that you will lead
- Keep a check on your actions by reviewing them regularly at your team meetings
- Record the progress that you and your team make with your Team Action Plan

	ACTION	PROGRESS MADE/COMPLETED	DATE
1			
2			
3			
4			
5			

9   Continuous Professional Development

Introduction

Welcome to Module 9, the final Module in the Best Practice Guide for Customer Service Managers. The aim in this module is to focus on you as the Manager or Team Leader, and how you can develop your own skills and knowledge. As you will see, you should try to use a wide range of methods of acquiring knowledge and developing skills and competencies in order to lead your team to that customer focused goal.

9.1   Learning outcomes

Learning Outcomes for Module 9
On successfully completing this module you should be able to: • Recognise the importance of Leadership in inspiring teams to deliver excellent customer service • Show an understanding of an effective model for Personal and Professional Development of customer related skills and knowledge

9.2   Why Develop Yourself?

Winning More Business

By developing your professional capabilities - including your skills as a Customer Service Manager or Team Leader - you can win more business and contribute to the success of your organisation. Remember that every organisation needs success; this success is built on reputation, and to keep that reputation as high as possible, your customers need to be delighted and made to feel special. It is your responsibility as a Customer Service Manager or Team Leader to:

- Equip and motivate your team to provide the best possible standards of service to your customers
- Keep existing customers loyal by meeting and exceeding their expectations
- Adopt a positive and professional attitude at all times, setting an example for your team members as the Manager or Team Leader
- Work with your colleagues and other managers to ensure your team functions well for all customers
- Be innovative and aware of new opportunities to raise the standards of service

The Role of the Customer Service Manager or Team Leader

As a Customer Service Manager or Team Leader, take responsibility for your own professional development, and make full use of your talents. Sir Richard Branson, Chairman of the Virgin group of companies, says, "People who work at Virgin are special. They aren't sheep. They think for themselves. They have good ideas and I listen to them. What is the point of hiring bright people if you don't use their talent? One of the things I try and do at Virgin is make people think about themselves and see themselves more positively. I firmly believe that anything is possible. I tell them, 'Believe in yourself. You can do it.' "

Make full use of your talents

Developing Your Professional Capabilities

Let's look at how you can identify your strengths and weaknesses in customer related skills. Writing a Personal Vision Statement allows you to include some of your own, personal objectives and ideas within your professional development, as well as meeting your organisation's vision. Then you can choose from a range of ways to actually implement those development needs. All those elements put together will help you to develop as a Customer Service Manager or Team Leader, providing excellent service to your team and your customers – and ultimately winning more business for the organisation.

Planning Your Personal and Professional Development

Plan and review your own training and development activities regularly. Keep to your organisation's process for this. For example, your organisation may have a well-established Appraisal Review System in place. If so, make full use of this method of reviewing your own development needs with your manager. However, such processes in some organisations do not give enough focus to customer service skills and knowledge, and it is important for Managers and

Team Leaders to plan and review their personal and professional development very regularly. You should have your own Professional Development Plan, which can be updated, say, monthly. In this way you can be highly responsive to the needs of your team, keeping the focus on customers, internal and external. Encourage your team members to adopt a similar approach.

Information needed for Professional Development Planning can come from these sources:

- Training and development needs identified at routine appraisals with your own manager
- Skills needs identified as a result of new activities—these could include projects, contracts, and changes in allocations of work within the team and the organisation
- Improvement needs that have been identified during day-to-day work with customers
- Whole-organisation initiatives and objectives, such as a drive to improve overall customer service

Personal and Professional Development Planning: Your Personal Vision Statement

Your Personal Vision Statement guides your life. A Personal Vision Statement can provide the direction necessary to guide your career, your personal life and your professional development. Since your Manager or Team Leader job role is inevitably inter-twined with your personal life, it makes sense to clarify and focus on the priorities for developing both aspects of your life. This can also improve your work-life balance, since it will enable you to take an holistic approach, rather than making the common mistake of trying to fit too much into the two "halves" of your life – your work and your personal life.

BEST PRACTICE
GCU Finance – A Personal Vision Statement

Sandra Gonzales, GCU's Director of Customer Service, has written her Personal Vision Statement.

My Vision:

- I will continuously develop my performance, skills and knowledge
- I am personally committed to ensuring that all my customers, both within and outside GCU, receive as high a level of service as possible.
- I intend to run a half-marathon within the next year
- I will lead the improvement of customer service in GCU to become recognised as the best financial services company in the world for customer service by 2010

When you are part of any organisation, you bring your own deeply held values and beliefs to the organisation. There they mix with the values of the other members to create an Organisational Culture, and this culture which pervades an organisation is an important element in how it operates. You might have noticed that organisations can differ very much in their organisational culture – it is often something which marks out the organisation as being different from others, and can be a major reason why people like, or dislike, working for that organisation.

Identifying and Establishing Your Values

Your values are made up of everything that has happened to you in your life and include influences from your parents and family, your religious affiliation, your friends and peers, your education, your reading, and more. Highly effective people recognise these environmental influences and identify and develop a clear but concise set of values and priorities. Once defined, your values can impact every aspect of your life:

- You demonstrate your values in action in your personal and work behaviours, decision making, and interaction with others
- You use your values to make decisions about priorities in your daily work and home life
- Your goals and life purpose are grounded in your values

Choose the values that are most important to you, the values you believe in and the ones that define your character.

WORK-BASED ACTIVITY
Personal Vision Statement

Using the ideas that you have read about, try creating your own Personal Vision Statement. It does not have to be long, but should reflect your own ideas and values.

My Personal Vision:

Develop a Credo for Your Team

One effective way of communicating an organisation's service concept is to use a Credo. This is a great way of letting all employees know about customer service, and of guiding professionals in their work with customers. Look at the next Best Practice example of a Credo from Unicentro. Relate it to your own organisation's values, vision or Service Concept, and try developing something similar with your own team.

BEST PRACTICE
Unicentro – A Service Credo

Delivering Excellent Service to External Customers

- I am personally responsible for the delivery of excellent service to my customers
- I am knowledgeable, skilled, motivated and professional in my delivery of customer service
- I take personal responsibility for any problems, resolve them to the customer's satisfaction, learn from them, and improve future service delivery
- I am an ambassador for my organisation with my customers

Delivering Excellent Service to Internal Customers

- I treat my colleagues with respect and professionalism at all times
- I challenge any barriers that hinder the delivery of excellent service
- I am proactive in helping to build a customer focused culture in my team

Understanding Customers' Needs

- I build relationships with my customers, based on both personal interaction and a deep understanding of their business needs
- I try to understand my customers' changing needs and respond appropriately
- I see every touch-point with customers as an opportunity to deliver excellent service

KNOWLEDGE-CHECK 9.1
GCU Finance - Professional Development Planning

At GCU Finance, Personal and Professional Development Planning is encouraged for all employees. Emma Murray, a Team Coach with GCU, is reviewing her own development needs. How often do you think a Manager or Team Leader such as Emma should review and update their Personal and Professional Development Plan?

⊙ Select the best answer to the question:

A ○ Regularly, according to need

B ○ Once a year, in line with the standard appraisal review process

C ○ Once a week

WORK-BASED ACTIVITY

Self Assessment - Personal and Professional Development

Complete this self assessment of your own Personal and Professional Development. If possible, involve your own manager and/or colleagues in this self assessment.

◉ Select **Consistently**, **Partly** or **Not at all** for each Performance Statement

	Consistently	Partly	Not at all
DEVELOPING MY SKILLS AND KNOWLEDGE:			
I make regular plans for improving my knowledge and skills	O	O	O
My skills and knowledge match my Manager or Team Leader role	O	O	O
MANAGING MY TIME AND WORKLOAD:			
I use an effective method of time management	O	O	O
At busy times I delegate and/or gain help from others	O	O	O
MAXIMISING MY LEARNING OPPORTUNITIES:			
I proactively seek to learn from others	O	O	O
I use collaborative web tools such as journals, mailing lists, blogs and wikis to learn from others	O	O	O

Your Self Assessment Score

Calculate your total score for the self assessment using:

Consistently = 2   Partly = 1   Not at all = 0

YOU SCORED	SELF ASSESSMENT ANALYSIS
0 to 4	Your development needs are not being met at present. Make your Personal and Professional Development a priority.
5 to 8	You are aware of the need for Personal and Professional Development, but should consider a wider range of development methods.
9 to 12	Congratulations - you are making use of a good range of Personal and Professional Development methods.

Identify Your Key Issues from this Self Assessment:

9.3 Leadership

Leadership

Effective leaders generally have these characteristics:

- They have followers who can trust and feel supported by the leader

- They have a clear vision of the future and set the direction for their team

- They show commitment and enthusiasm, helping to lead people through times of change

- They communicate honestly and openly, listening and talking to their team

- They empower people, giving their team the authority and confidence to get the job done

Leaders.. have a clear vision of the future

Thinking About Leadership

There are different ideas about the concept of Leadership. Some definitions of Leadership are:

- A position of office associated with technical skill or experience

- The quality that a person or collection of people hold in which they command respect and are highly influential

- Guidance or direction, as in the phrase, "The President is not providing enough leadership"

- Influencing others for some purpose

Think about these (and other) ideas about what Leadership means. Now record your own ideas of how an inspirational leader could raise the profile of customer service in a team or organisation.

Leadership and Customer Service in My Team/Organisation:

Is There a Difference Between Management and Leadership?

Recognise that there are differences between Management and Leadership. Management is about running an operation or function - about getting the right people and resources in the right place at the right time.

Typical Management responsibilities include:

- Planning, negotiating, setting and controlling budgets

- Recruiting staff

- Allocating work to teams and individuals

- Problem solving

- Carrying out the procedures of the organisation

Leadership is more inspirational. It involves creating a vision and gaining people's commitment. As a leader you will probably being doing these activities:

- Setting the overall direction of the team or organisation

- Creating a sense of purpose

- Inspiring people to achieve objectives

- Motivating people to work hard for customers

- Encouraging people to have the determination to overcome barriers

The reality is that an effective Manager or Team Leader needs both aspects – Management and Leadership. Try to learn from others how to be an effective manager and leader.

Do I Need Charisma?

People talk about leaders needing charisma. It can be useful - not everyone has it naturally, but it is not essential! Charisma is rather a blunt weapon – it is easy to use it too much and then to rely on it. In reality a wide range of management skills needs to be developed.

Charisma tends to allow a manager to dominate people and it can result in an inappropriate type of management. The best organisations empower their people to take their own decisions, rather than relying heavily on charismatic leaders.

In reality a range of management skills need to be developed

9.4   Managing Your Time

Developing Your Manager Performance

Take time out regularly to look at your own performance as a Manager or Team Leader. Identify your priorities for development, and plan these into your work – whether it be training, gaining a qualification, or simply allowing sufficient time for reflecting on the key tasks ahead. It is vital that you are self-aware, and put into place whatever is needed to raise your performance and confidence as a Manager or Team Leader.

Time Management

All Managers and Team Leaders need effective Time Management. We have busy jobs and there are many demands on our time. Unless you can develop ways of managing your time and dealing with things in the right order of priorities you could find yourself continually "fire-fighting."

How is Your Time Spent?

Look back through your diary to work out how you spend your time. If you have not kept a diary, log your activities for a couple of weeks to see where your time is going. You will be amazed how useful this simple activity is. You will probably be surprised that you spend so much time on some things and so little on others. The trick is to spend the right time on the right things! Look in your diary or log at:

- How much time was planned and how much was unplanned
- How accurate your planning was - did you complete tasks in the planned time?
- How much time was spent on routine tasks that could have been delegated
- How much time was wasted in unhelpful interruptions
- Whether you have spent too much time dealing with emails
- What are your best and worst times of the day and week for getting tasks done?

What are Your Problem Areas?

Ask yourself why you are using some of your time inefficiently. You could split problems into external time wasters and the internal time-wasters. External time-wasters include factors beyond your immediate control, such as mistakes or inefficiencies of other departments and unexpected extra work. Internal time-wasters will include personal inefficiency, poor planning, lack of assertiveness in turning away unwanted callers, and putting off problems and the activities that you just don't like doing. (By the way we all tend to do the jobs that we most enjoy first – even if they are not priorities. If you plan properly you can reduce this natural tendency).

Take time .. to look at your own performance as a Manager

Clarify your Objectives and Priorities

Make sure you know your job description. It tells you what you should and should not be doing. Agree your role, objectives and targets with your own manager, and discuss it with your team as well. Everyone will at least then know what is expected of you.

Tackle the External Time-Wasters

If you find that problem relationships and reaction to situations beyond your control take up too much of your time, try to minimise this by:

- Reviewing and improving how your team deals with problems
- Asking colleagues to be concise when giving written or oral reports

Tackle the Internal Time-Wasters

Do the following in order to make better use of your valuable time:

- Plan your activities for a week ahead – then spend a few minutes each morning reviewing and adjusting your plan
- Build slack time into your plan to deal with the unexpected
- Prioritise your work – and be as objective as possible in this
- Be firm but polite in declining tasks that are not your responsibility

- Focus on the tasks that cannot be delegated to someone else
- Work smartly – using technology in particular to help organise your priorities
- Train or coach your team members to manage their time effectively too

Find the Time to Relax

Overwork is counter-productive. It causes stress and reduces your efficiency. Value your own health and happiness, and recognise that everyone needs time to relax. Understand that your personal life, mental attitude and physical fitness have a big impact on your ability to do the job effectively.

GUIDE-LINE
Time Management Dos and Don'ts

DO:

- Clarify your customer service objectives and targets
- Assess priorities and constantly review them as circumstances change
- Be firm and assertive with unwanted time stealers
- Make sure your time plan is efficient but realistic

DON'T:

- Equate being busy with being efficient
- Attempt to do more than you are capable of
- Give priority to the loudest claim on your time - it may not be the most important
- Assume your plans are rigid - environments and situations change and you will need to adapt
- See time management as purely a work issue - it is a personal issue, and spans your work-life balance

KNOWLEDGE-CHECK 9.2
Unicentro - Time Management

Stephanie Osario, a Unicentro Team Coach, is having a busy day dealing with a wide range of different tasks. Sometimes, balancing priorities can be difficult.

A Team Member comes into Stephanie Osario's office, asking for a discussion about a personal issue which is concerning him. Stephanie starts the discussion, and then the telephone rings – it is Miss Gulrajani, a loyal retail customer, who is demanding the immediate resolution of a problem. Which is the best course of action for Stephanie Osario?

◉   Select the best answer to the question:

A ○   Take the details from Miss Gulrajani and say she will call the customer back within 15 minutes to resolve the problem

B ○   Tell the team member to come back later when Miss Gulrajani's problem has been resolved

C ○   Give the team member the chance to improve his own skills by dealing with Miss Gulrajani's problem

9.5   Professional Development

Professional Development Planning for Customer Related Skills

When you include customer related skills in your Professional Development Planning, there are different methods of actually implementing your development needs:

- Informal Learning through websites, intranets, journals, and other media
- E-Learning and Blended Learning programmes
- Learning on the job, for example Coaching, or shadowing
- Instructor-led training courses
- Team development activities

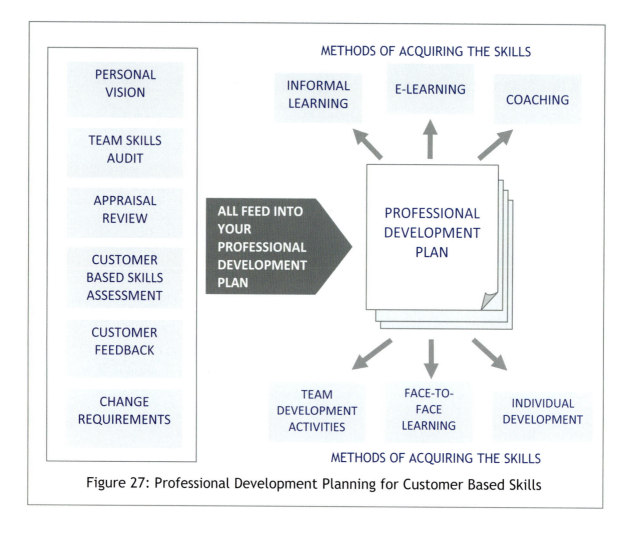

Figure 27: Professional Development Planning for Customer Based Skills

BEST PRACTICE
Unicentro – Recording Learning

Informal Learning

Some of the main methods of implementing the requirements of the Professional Development Plan are given below, using examples provided by Unicentro employees.

Informal Learning

At Unicentro, Jane Dupree, Manager of the Marketing Unit, regularly reads journals and online magazines related to Marketing. She also attends monthly meetings of the professional marketing institute that she is a member of. These are just a few examples of her informal learning.

Coaching

Sanjay Patel, Unicentro's Finance Director, recently recruited a new member for his accounts team. She was new to the accounting system, so Sanjay organised regular coaching sessions over a two-month period to speed up her learning of the job. As the coaching sessions progressed, Sanjay also took the chance to help the new employee with her customer service skills, as she had been put forward to be the accounts team's representative on the Customer Service Framework Improvement Group.

Instructor-Led Training

All of Unicentro's new employees are inducted in customer service skills within their first two weeks at the company. Following this the company holds an annual Customer Focus Update—a one-day workshop which is designed to give all employees new ideas when trying to improve their relationships with customers. These face-to-face training sessions are delivered by skilled instructors who are subject matter experts in customer service.

Team Development Activities

Simon Brasher, ICT Help Desk Manager at Unicentro, held a team development day recently. The various activities during the day included a brainstorming session on how to "go the extra mile" for customers, and a Service Recovery simulation in which pairs of team members role-played. One took the part of a customer with a problem and the partner was a Customer Service Professional trying to identify the problem and suggest possible methods of resolution. The whole of the IT support team attended. The event was successful in helping to improve the team's internal customer service ratings.

E-Learning and Blended Learning

Simon Brasher is always sitting at a computer. It is only natural that he should conduct much of his learning and development through that medium. As well as the considerable informal learning he achieves through the Internet, he also completed several e-learning modules to increase his knowledge and understanding of computer networks. This gave him a qualification and also helped when he had to assist with the installation of Unicentro's new wide area network. At Unicentro, Jane Dupree, Manager of the Marketing Unit, regularly reads journals and online magazines related to Marketing. She also attends monthly meetings of the professional marketing institute that she is a member of. These are just a few examples of her informal learning.

GUIDE-LINE
Top Tips for E-Learning and Blended Learning

1. Get to Know the Course

Spend time at the start familiarising yourself with the course, its structure and its tools and resources. Purchase any other required resources - such as textbooks - well in advance. Resolve any technology issues early on so that you don't fall behind.

2. Draw up a Study Schedule

Draw up your study schedule, showing the times you will devote to your e-learning - taking into account all your other commitments, such as your Manager or Team Leader role, career, family, hobbies and social engagements.

3. Understand Your Motivators

Find out what motivates you to learn - especially when it becomes difficult. Examples of motivators could be the satisfaction of completing a module, or promising yourself a small reward after a study session - for instance, "Once I have completed this assignment I'll watch a film or go to see my friends."

Break down your course into manageable and achievable chunks. If it's already modular then you can even break each module down further into study session, aligning these with your study schedule.

4. Find a Mentor

You are more likely to keep on track if a colleague or mentor knows about your e-learning course and why you are doing it. Gain the support of a mentor - this could be an informal arrangement - or ask friends to check up on you, ensuring you keep to your study schedule.

5. Make Use of Your Online Tutor

Make full use of the expertise and advice of your online tutor. Contact your tutor with any questions well in advance of due dates, remembering that they may not respond immediately. Ask about your progress, and seek feedback whenever you can.

6. Celebrate Your Achievements

Be proud of your accomplishments. Review the results of quizzes. Learn from your mistakes and celebrate your successes.

7. Maximise Your Learning

Take notes. Imagine questions that might be on a test from your study guide, from your textbook, from films or audio tapes. Read your textbook and other assigned reading. Watch the video material if required. Don't substitute one for the other or assume class notes on the web are enough. Test questions will be taken from all sources.

8. Use Your Learning

Put your learning into practice as soon as you can. Don't wait until after the course has finished - the best learning is achieved through doing, so putting the changes and improvement into place in your customer service team will help consolidate and develop your learning to a deeper level.

9.6   Professional Membership

As a Manager or Team Leader of customer service, you have a key responsibility to deliver, on behalf of your team and organisation, the best possible service to both external and internal customers. Your professional knowledge and skills are critical to this responsibility, and so you should consider membership of appropriate professional bodies and/or institutes which champion the cause of customer service. Of course, the sector in which you work may have professional bodies which are useful to you, or it may be more appropriate to belong to a specific customer service institute.

In the UK the Institute of Customer Service is the organisation which drives forward the concept of professionalism in customer service.   Its mission is to lead customer service performance and professionalism. It has a large number of members, both individual and corporate. Other countries also have their own customer service institutes.   Other options for professional membership could include membership of an institute devoted to management, or one which represents the specific sector for your organisation.

Typical benefits of professional membership include:

- Collaboration with like-minded professionals from other organisations
- Ability to benchmark individual performance against other organisations, helping you see what best practice looks like and apply it to your own situations
- Exposure to new ideas on customer service – for example through networking, attending master classes and case study visits
- Involvement in discussion and debate around key customer service topics
- References to information about customer service
- Attendance at seminars, conferences and other events related to customer service issues
- Training and development programmes and resources
- Standards for customer service – both organisational and individual
- Tools to help your identify service levels and service gaps
- Jobs boards and other resources for career development

9.7   Using the Internet

The wide range of collaborative tools available on the internet provide an incredible wealth of information and ideas. Customer service practitioners of all types, whether Professionals, Managers or Team Leaders, many of these resources can add to your knowledge and understanding of customer service. You are missing out if you do not take advantage of this vast and rapidly developing pool of knowledge. If you do choose to access and use the knowledge and collaborative opportunities within the internet, this can accelerate your customer service learning at a high rate.

Think about some of the internet-based tools that are available, often at no financial cost:

- Glossaries and encyclopaedias relating to customer service
- Online journals
- News feeds which you can set up to automatically seek and send you items of interest about Service related peer reviewed articles
- Business reports on customer service issues
- Discussion forums and news groups
- Opportunities to contribute to a discussion or forum on a customer service topic
- News items reporting recent developments or examples of good and bad practice in customer service

9.8   End-of-Module Knowledge-Check

KNOWLEDGE-CHECK 9.3

⦿   Select the best answer to the question:

1   A Personal Vision Statement would normally:

  A ○ Include personal and professional objectives

  B ○ Not include professional objectives

  C ○ Include personal but not professional objectives

2   When a Manager or Team Leader reviews their Professional Development Plan, this should be done:

  A ○ As often as is appropriate

  B ○ As regularly as possible

  C ○ As often as the organisation's appraisal review process is conducted

3   One key feature of Leadership which distinguishes it from Management is the ability to:

  A ○ Organise others

  B ○ Inspire others

  C ○ Be an efficient administrator

4   An Organisation's Culture is determined by:

  A ○ The mix of values of different people in the organisation

  B ○ The Directors of the organisation

  C ○ The Shareholders of the organisation

5   A Manager or Team Leader's Time Management should be seen as:

  A ○ An ability which cannot be learned or improved

  B ○ A purely work-based issue

  C ○ An issue which spans the work-life balance

9.9   Team Action Plan and Progress Record

Team Action Plan

Now you need to plan your areas for change.

- Write below the actions that you intend to take over the coming weeks and months

- Share the plans with your team to make sure they are all on board with the changes and improvements that you will lead

- Keep a check on your actions by reviewing them regularly at your team meetings

- Record the progress that you and your team make with your Team Action Plan

	ACTION	PROGRESS MADE/COMPLETED	DATE
1			
2			
3			
4			
5			

Answers to Module Knowledge-Checks

Module 1

Knowledge-Check 1.1: B

Knowledge-Check 1.2: B

Knowledge-Check 1.3: A

Knowledge-Check 1.4: B,A,C,A,C

Module 3

Knowledge-Check 3.1: B

Knowledge-Check 3.2: C

Knowledge-Check 3.3: C,A,C,C,A

Module 5

Knowledge-Check 5.1: B

Knowledge-Check 5.2: A

Knowledge-Check 5.3: C

Knowledge-Check 5.4: B,C,C,C,A

Module 7

Knowledge-Check 7.1: A

Knowledge-Check 7.2: C

Knowledge-Check 7.3: A,C,A,A,C

Module 9

Knowledge-Check 9.1: A

Knowledge-Check 9.2: A

Knowledge-Check 9.3: A,A,B,A,C

Module 2

Knowledge-Check 2.1: B

Knowledge-Check 2.2: A

Knowledge-Check 2.3: C

Knowledge-Check 2.4: C,B,A,C,B

Module 4

Knowledge-Check 4.1: C

Knowledge-Check 4.2: C,C,C,C,A

Module 6

Knowledge-Check 6.1: A

Knowledge-Check 6.2: C

Knowledge-Check 6.3: A,B,A,A,B

Module 8

Knowledge-Check 8.1: B

Knowledge-Check 8.2: C,A,C,A,A

References

Books, Articles and Reports:

Accenture 2008 Global Customer Satisfaction Report: High Performance in the Age of Customer Centricity
Accenture, 2008, www.accenture.com/centricity

Berne, E.
Games People Play: The Psychology of Human Relationships
Ballantine Books, 1996, ISBN-13: 978-0345410030, ISBN-10: 0345410033

Cameron D.
Herzberg – Still a Key to Understanding Motivation
Training Officer, Vol 32 No 6, July/Aug 1996

Cook, S.
Customer Care Excellence: How to Create an Effective Customer Focus
Kogan Page Ltd, 2008, ISBN-13: 978-0749450663, ISBN-10: 0749450665

Edwards, S.
Best Practice Guide for Customer Service Professionals
Customer 1st International, 2006, ISBN-13: 978-0954874414, ISBN-10: 0954874412

Ells, H., Dutton, C., Frost, P.
Excellence in Managing the Business-to-Business Customer Relationship
Institute of Customer Service, 2006, ISBN-13: 978-1906080006

Daffy, C.
Once a Customer, Always a Customer
Oak Tree Press, 2000, ISBN-13: 978-1860761645, ISBN-10: 186076164X

Hill, N., Hampshire S.
Customer Priorities: What Customers Really Want
Institute of Customer Service, 2006, ISBN-10: 0953902889

Herzberg, F.
One More Time: How do you Motivate Employees?
Harvard Business Review, Vol 6 No 1, Jan/Feb 1968

National Occupational Standards for Customer Service
Institute of Customer Service, 2006, ISBN-13: , ISBN-10: 1900376024

Johns, Ted
World Class Customer Service: The What, The Why, The How
Institute of Customer Service, 2008, ISBN-13: 978-1906080037

Johnston, R.
Delivering Service Excellence: The View from the Front Line
Institute of Customer Service, 2003, ISBN-10: 0953902862

Johnston, R.
Service Excellence=Reputation=Profit: Developing and Sustaining a Reputation for Service Excellence
Institute of Customer Service, 2001, ISBN-13: 978-0953902842, ISBN-10: 0953902846

Johnston, R., Clark, G.
Service Operations Management: Improving Service Delivery
Financial Times/ Prentice Hall, 2005, ISBN-13: 978-0273683674, ISBN-10: 0273683675

Katzenbach, J.R., Douglas K. Smith, D.K.
The Discipline of Teams: What makes the difference between a team that performs and one that doesn't?
Harvard Business Review, Jul/Aug 2005, Vol. 83 Issue 7/8

Smith, S. and Wheeler, J.
Managing the Customer Experience: Turning Customers into Advocates
Financial Times/Prentice Hall, 2002, ISBN-13: 978-0273661955, ISBN-10: 0273661957

Websites:

www.customer1st.co.uk	Customer 1st International
www.customer1stlearning.co.uk	Customer 1st International's Learning Website
www.instituteofcustomerservice.com	Institute of Customer Service
www.customerserviceawards.com	Customer Service Awards
www.mycustomer.com	MyCustomer.com
www.ukcsi.com	UK Customer Satisfaction Index

Mapping to National Occupational Standards for Customer Service

UNIT 7 (THEME: CUSTOMER SERVICE FOUNDATIONS)
Understand customer service to improve service delivery

Knowledge item		Section(s)
7.1	**use accepted customer service language and apply its principles**	
7.1.1	explain how your organisation builds a Service Offer that will meet customer expectations	1.4/1.5/3.6
7.1.2	describe how the Service Offer is affected by financial and other resource limitations	1.5/1.6/4.9
7.1.3	describe what effects the Service Offer may have on the service chain	7.6
7.1.4	give examples of how customers may form their expectations of the services or products	1.3/1.4
7.1.5	explain the importance of effective teamwork and service partnerships for the delivery of excellent customer service	1.8/7.6
7.1.6	give examples of the similarities and differences in planning customer Service Offers for the commercial, public sector and private sector not-for-profit organisations	7.6
7.1.7	explain how customer service can provide added value to a public sector or private sector not-for profit organisation	6.2
7.1.8	explain how customer service can provide a competitive advantage for a commercial organisation	1.6
7.1.9	explain why your organisation must limit the level of customer service it gives in order to balance customer satisfaction with organisational goals	2.2
7.1.10	explain how your behaviour and the behaviour of customers can influence the level of customer satisfaction achieved	1.5/6.4
7.1.11	give positive examples of how you deal with different customer behaviours and personalities when managing problems and complaints	6.4/6.5/6.6
7.1.12	explain the importance of effective communication in the delivery of excellent customer service	1.5/2.7/5.3
7.1.13	give examples of how you ensure that communication with diverse groups of customers is effective and efficient	2.7/5.3/5.6
7.1.14	explain the significance of continuous improvement within customer service and the way that change and the management of change are central to ongoing customer satisfaction	7.3
7.2	**place customer service principles in context for your professional customer service role**	
7.2.1	give examples of approaches different sectors may take to customer service	2.4/3.6
7.2.2	explain your organisation's policies and procedures for the delivery of services or products and why it is important to follow them	1.9
7.2.3	give examples of the Service Offer of competitors of your organisation or explain how your organisation's Service Offer is benchmarked if it is not in a competitive environment	1.3
7.2.4	give examples of the essential features and benefits of your organisation's services or products that influence customer service delivery and satisfaction	1.3
7.2.5	describe how your organisation balances its needs with customer expectations and needs	2.2/3.5
7.2.6	explain the ethical and values base of your organisation's approach to customer service	2.3

UNIT 8 (THEME: CUSTOMER SERVICE FOUNDATIONS)
Know the rules to follow when developing customer service

Knowledge item		Section(s)
8.1	**develop customer service following organisational rules and procedures**	
8.1.1	describe organisational policies and procedures that you would need to take into account to propose improvements or developments to customer service	1.9/8.6
8.1.2	describe how you would obtain authorisation to change customer service practices	1.9/8.6
8.1.3	explain the limits of your own authority and who else in the organisation would need to be involved if additional authority is needed for improvements or developments	1.9/8.6
8.1.4	explain how you would involve colleagues or service partners in the implementation of improvements or changes	1.9/7.6/8.6
8.2	**develop customer service following external regulation and legislation**	
8.2.1	explain relevant regulation and legislation relating to consumer protection	1.9
8.2.2	describe relevant regulation and legislation relating to data protection	1.9
8.2.3	explain relevant regulation and legislation relating to disability discrimination and equal opportunities	1.9
8.2.4	explain relevant regulation and legislation relating to diversity and inclusion and discrimination for reasons other than disability	1.9
8.2.5	explain relevant regulation and legislation relating to health and safety of customers and colleagues	1.9
8.2.6	explain the need to balance the requirements of regulation with the needs and objectives of your organisation	1.9
8.2.7	describe how you would incorporate relevant regulation and legislation when planning and implementing improvements and developments	2.2/8.6

UNIT 13 (THEME : IMPRESSION AND IMAGE)
Make customer service personal

Knowledge item		Section(s)
13a	how use of your customer's name makes service more personal	4.5
13b	personality types and their receptiveness to personalised ser vices	4.5/6.5
13c	types of personal information about customers that should and should not be kept on record	1.9/5.6
13d	features of personal service that are most appreciated by customers with individual needs	5.6
13e	body language and approaches to communication that are generally interpreted as open	3.5/4.5
13f	your organisation's guidelines on actions that are permissible outside of the normal routines and procedures	1.9/8.6
13g	your own preferences and comfort levels relating to how you are willing and able to personalise service	5.6

UNIT 14 (THEME : IMPRESSION AND IMAGE)
Go the extra mile in customer service

Knowledge item		Section(s)
14a	your organisation's Service Offer	1.3
14b	how customers form expectations of the service they will receive	1.3
14c	what types of service action most customers will see as adding value to the customer service they have already had	1.6
14d	your organisation's rules and procedures that determine your authority to 'go the extra mile'	1.9
14e	relevant legislation and regulation that impact on your freedom to 'go the extra mile'	1.9/8.6
14f	how your organisation receives customer ser vice feedback on the types of customer experience that has impressed them	3.5/3.6
14g	your organisation's procedures for making changes in its Service Offer	1.3/1.9

UNIT 23 (THEME : DELIVERY)
Recognise diversity when delivering customer service

Knowledge item		Section(s)
23a	the importance of recognising diversity in relation to age, disability, national origin, religion, sexual orientation, values, ethnic culture, education, lifestyle, beliefs, physical appearance, social class and economic status	5.6
23b	reasons why consideration of diversity and inclusion issues affect customer service	5.6
23c	organisational guidelines to make customer service inclusive for diverse groups of customers	5.6
23d	legal use and meaning of the word 'reasonable'	1.9
23e	how to observe and interpret non-verbal clues	3.5/4.5
23f	how to listen actively for clues about your customer's expectations and needs	3.5
23g	techniques for obtaining additional information from customers through tactful and respectful questions	3.5
23h	behaviour that might cause offence to specific groups of people to whom you regularly provide customer service	4.5/5.6
23i	how to impress specific groups of people to whom you regularly provide customer service	5.6

UNIT 25 (THEME : DELIVERY)
Organise the delivery of reliable customer service

Knowledge item		Section(s)
25a	organisational procedures for unexpected situations and your role within them	1.9/4.10
25b	resource implications in times of staff sickness and holiday periods and your responsibility at these times	4.10
25c	the importance of having reliable and fast information for your customers and your organisation	1.3/1.4/5.3
25d	organisational procedures and systems for delivering customer service	4.10
25e	how to identify useful customer feedback and how to decide which feedback should be acted on	3.5
25f	how to communicate feedback from customers to others	3.5
25g	organisational procedures and systems for recording, storing, retrieving and supplying customer ser vice information.	3.5/4.10
25h	legal and regulatory requirements regarding the storage of data	1.9

UNIT 32   (THEME : HANDLING PROBLEMS)
Monitor and solve customer service problems

Knowledge item		Section(s)
32a	organisational procedures and systems for dealing with customer service problems	1.9/6.3/6.5
32b	organisational procedures and systems for identifying repeated customer service problems	6.6
32c	how the successful resolution of customer service problems contributes to customer loyalty with the external customer and improved working relationships with service partners or internal customers	1.4/6.2
32d	how to negotiate with and reassure customers while their problems are being solved	6.4/6.5

UNIT 33   (THEME : HANDLING PROBLEMS)
Apply risk assessment to customer service

Knowledge item		Section(s)
33a	your organisation's customer service process and the moments of truth (those points in the customer service process that have most impact on the customer experience)	1.9/4.10/6.4
33b	risk assessment techniques	6.3
33c	how to evaluate risk according to probability of occurrence and consequences of occurrence	6.3
33d	the nature of potential customer service risks including financial, reputational and health and safety risks	6.3
33e	cost/benefit analysis	6.3
33f	SWOT (Strengths, Weaknesses, Opportunities, Threats) and PE STLE (Political, Economic, Social, Technological, Legal, Environmental) analysis	6.3

UNIT 34   (THEME : HANDLING PROBLEMS)
Process customer service complaints

Knowledge item		Section(s)
34a	how to monitor the level of complaints and identify those that should provoke a special review of the ser vice offer and service delivery	6.6
34b	why dealing with complaints is an inevitable part of delivering customer service	6.6
34c	organisational procedures for dealing with complaints	6.6
34d	how to negotiate a solution with your customer that is acceptable to that customer and to the organisation	6.5/6.6
34e	the regulatory definition of a complaint in your sector and the regulatory requirements of how complaints should be handled and reported	1.9/6.6
34f	when to escalate a complaint by involving more senior members of the organisation or an independent third party	1.9/6.6
34g	the implications of admitting liability for an error made by your organisation	1.9/6.6
34h	how to spot and interpret signals that your customer may be considering making a complaint	6.3
34i	techniques for handling conflict	6.5
34j	the importance of dealing with a complaint promptly	6.3/6.6
34k	why the offer of compensation or replacement service or products may not always be the best options for resolving a complaint	6.6
34l	how the successful handling of a complaint presents an opportunity to impress a customer who has been dissatisfied	1.3/6.2

UNIT 39　　(THEME : DEVELOPMENT AND IMPROVEMENT)
Work with others to improve customer service

Knowledge item		Section(s)
39a	who else is involved either directly or indirectly in the delivery of customer service	8.2
39b	the roles and responsibilities of others in your organisation	4.7
39c	the roles of others outside your organisation who have an impact on your services or products	7.6
39d	what the goals or targets of your organisation are in relation to customer service and how these are set	2.2/2.3/2.4
39e	how your organisation identifies improvements in customer service	8.2/8.6

UNIT 40　　(THEME : DEVELOPMENT AND IMPROVEMENT)
Promote continuous improvement in customer service

Knowledge item		Section(s)
40a	how service improvements in your area affect the balance between overall customer satisfaction, the costs of providing service and regulatory requirements	8.3
40b	how customer experience is influenced by the way service is delivered	1.2/1.3/1.4
40c	how to collect, analyse and present customer feedback	3.5
40d	how to make a business case to others to bring about change in the products or services you offer	8.6

UNIT 41　　(THEME : DEVELOPMENT AND IMPROVEMENT)
Develop your own and others' customer service skills

Knowledge item		Section(s)
41a	organisational systems and procedures for developing your own and others' personal performance in customer ser vice	4.2 4.3
41b	how your behaviour impacts on others	4.5/4.6/5.4
41c	how to review effectively your personal strengths and development needs	4.6/9.2/9.5
41d	how to put together a personal development plan for yourself or a colleague that will build on strengths and overcome weaknesses in areas that are important to customer service	9.5
41e	how to obtain useful and constructive personal feedback from others	9.2/9.5
41f	how to respond positively to personal feedback	4.6/9.5
41g	how to put together a coaching plan that will build on the strengths of the learner and overcome their weaknesses in areas that are important to customer service and their job role	4.4/4.6
41h	how to give useful and constructive personal feedback to others	9.2/9.5
41i	how to help others to respond positively to personal feedback	9.2/9.5

UNIT 42   (THEME : DEVELOPMENT AND IMPROVEMENT)
Lead a team to improve customer service

Knowledge item		Section(s)
42a	the roles and responsibilities of your team members and where they fit in with the overall structure of the organisation	4.7
42b	how team and individual performance can affect the achievement of organisational objectives	1.8/2.4/5.2
42c	the implications of failure to improve customer service for your team members and your organisation	1.5/1.6/7.3
42d	how to plan work activities	9.4
42e	how to present plans to others to gain understanding and commitment	5.3
42f	how to facilitate meetings to encourage frank and open discussion	5.3
42g	how to involve and motivate staff to encourage teamwork	5.4/5.5/5.8
42h	how to recognise and deal sensitively with issues of underperformance	5.3/5.4/5.8

Glossary

Accessibility

A service characteristics which includes, for example, being flexible and having service available at as many times and locations as possible.

Action-Centred Leadership

A simple checklist approach to planning tasks. It helps a Manager to identify the key aspects of any task which a team may be taking on or planning. Using a checklist approach (Task-Team-Individual), the Manager the three aspects: how the task will be undertaken, how the team will develop through completing it, and how the task can benefit the development of individual team members. In applying Action-Centred Leadership to a customer service team in particular, the manager should also consider the implications for customers.

Active Listening

Making a conscious, planned effort to apply specific listening skills. It is a skill that can be developed and involves asking well planned questions to ensure that one really understands customers' and team members' needs and expectations. Feedback can also be given, perhaps through gestures and body language, to reinforce the fact that the listener is understanding what is being communicated.

Added Value

Added Value is the extra, over and above the basic product or Service Offer that an organisation makes available to its customers. This added value represents extra benefits that can truly delight customers and keep them loyal.

Aggressive Behaviour

A type of behaviour in which one disregards the feelings and views of others.

Appraisal Review System

A structured approach to reviewing and planning of an individual team member's work and development, usually through regular, one-to-one meetings between the individual and his or her Manager.

Assertive Behaviour

A type of behaviour in which one acts in an adult manner, applying thinking and reasoning. If one acts assertively one puts one's own point across in a clear, firm, but fair manner.

Assurance

A service quality factor - the knowledge and courtesy of the employees and their ability to convey trust and confidence.

Augmented Service

A level of service which goes beyond core service and is the minimum your organisation should provide in order to at least keep up with the market. You will generally be meeting and exceeding customers' expectations. Augmented Service will retain many customers in the short and medium term, but this level of service does not consistently deliver really exceptional experiences for customers - the "Wow!" factor is not there all the time.

B2B

A Business-to-Business organisation; the customer is another business rather than an individual.

Barrier To Change

Any obstacle which may prevent the implementation of a planned change.

Belief Cycle

A vicious circle (of Belief, Attitude, Behaviour and Outcome), which can be broken by consciously changing one's attitude and therefore modifying one's tendency to behave in a particular way. This concept is useful for an individual dealing with a difficult situation or person.

Benchmark

In customer service a benchmark is the service level or quality attained by another organisation, which may be used to compare performance and to set targets. For example a team could benchmark its own customer service ratings against the levels achieved by the best organisation in the sector.

Blended Learning

A mixture of different learning types, often applied to the combination of e-learning or distance learning with some face-to-face interaction with tutors/trainers and/or other learners.

Body Language

We communicate using words but they don't usually tell the whole story. Body language is a collection of expressions on our face and gestures we make. Very often body language tells us more about what somebody is actually thinking than the words they use. When you are dealing with a customer you can learn a lot about what they thinking from their body language. This also means that you need to be aware of the messages you are giving to the customer through your own expressions and gestures – your own body language.

Business Case

A clear justification, usually including financial details, of why a specific proposal, investment or change is worthwhile from an organisational viewpoint.

Circle of Frustration

A vicious circle, often applied to delegation, in which a Manager can tend to delegate repetitive, undemanding tasks to individuals, who find the delegated tasks boring, and therefore fail to improve their own skills and motivation. The Manager then sees the individual as someone who is low-skilled and poorly motivated.

Coaching

Working with another individual to help them develop their skills and knowledge. It is normally carried out one-to-one, with the coach identifying and signposting the support and resources that the individual needs in order to develop.

Code of Practice

Many trade associations and professional bodies have a Code of Practice that guides members on how they should conduct their business. Most Codes of Practice include guidance on how to deal with customers. In particular they usually cover how members should deal with complaints and customer problems. Codes of Practice do not have the same kind of authority as regulation and legislation. However, if a member always ignores a Code of Practice, the association or professional body may make it very difficult for that member to continue in business.

Committed Staff

An organisational competence which contributes to excellent customer service. I is characterised by employees who are well-motivated, have a can-do attitude, enjoy team working and supporting both internal and external customers.

Communication

A service characteristic important for service excellence which includes, for example, providing customers with good quality pre-purchase product information, information about after-sales service and accurate and timely information for internal customers.

Competence

A service characteristic important for service excellence which includes, for example, the efficient packaging of a number of items in a delivery and being an accurate advisor to customers.

Complaint Analysis

Gathering information about customer complaints in order to spot trends and identify where processes may be breaking down and therefore where improvements need to be made.

Components of Excellent Customer Service

The critical organisation competencies which are features of organisations which have actually achieved a reputation for excellent customer service.

Continuous Improvement

Many organisations try to keep ahead of competitors by providing better customer service. If competitors also do this, organisations have to keep improving their customer service to stay ahead. So the process of continuous improvement helps organisations to make sure this happens as a matter of routine. Customer service is delivered and customer feedback is collected. The customer feedback is used to measure customer expectations and customer satisfaction. The information from the customer feedback is used to find ways of improving the customer service and changes are made.

Contract Manager
A manager in an organisation who takes the lead in building and maintaining an ongoing relationship with a corporate customer.

Core Products and Services
The basic products and services offered to customers of an organisation, before consideration of any added value products and services.

Core Service
A level of service which provides the basic products and services, and will meet some customers' expectations. It is unlikely, however, to satisfy some customers - because they have experienced better service elsewhere.

Corporate Customer
Customer of an organisation who is another businesses rather than an individual.

Corporate Objectives
The key achievements which an organisation commits its resources to.

Cost Benefit Analysis
A method of assessing and quantifying, where possible, all the costs and benefits to an organisation or team of a particular change. It is often applied to investment decisions where a significant financial outlay is required. All tangible (measurable) costs and benefits should be estimated (usually in financial terms). Intangible costs and benefits – ones that are difficult or impossible to quantify – should be identified and listed in the analysis. If the benefits outweigh the costs (giving regard to the intangible ones), then the analysis shows that change is worthwhile.

Credo
A statement which sets out an organisation's values and approach to customer service, often used to guide professionals in their work with customers.

Customer Based Skills
The practical skills which are needed to meet and exceed the expectations of customers.

Customer Centric
Customer Centric activities are those that focus primarily on customers. Teams that deliver high levels of customer service tend to make many of their activities Customer Centric.

Customer Charter
Some organisations choose to tell customers about their Service Offer in a statement of what they will do for the customer and call it a customer charter. Some customer charters set out what the organisation will do to compensate a customer when customer service has not been delivered in line with the charter. A customer charter is a statement of intent and is generally not part of the contract that a service deliverer makes with its customer.

Customer Expectations
Customer expectations are what people think should happen and how they think they should be treated when asking for or receiving customer service.
Expectations are formed by:
- what people hear and see
- what they read and what the organisation tells them
- what happens during the customer experience
- what has happened to them in other customer service experiences.

Customer Experience
Customer experience is what a customer feels and remembers about the customer service that he or she has received. The customer experience of an individual customer service transaction affects the customer relationship and influences customer expectations for the future. When a customer is about to receive customer service his or her customer expectations are influenced by all the customer experiences that he or she has had in the past both with your organisation and with others.

Customer Feedback

Customer feedback is information about customer perceptions of customer service collected by the organisation from customers or given to the organisation by customers. Customer feedback can be collected formally using questionnaires or other kinds of surveys. Informal customer feedback can be collected from chance remarks or comments the customer has made with or without being asked.

Customer Focused Culture

A Customer Focused Culture applies in an organisation in which the customers (both external and internal) are central to the way the organisation does its business. Consideration of customers permeates the whole organisation, and employees are aware of the critical importance of customer service.

Customer Focused Processes

An organisational competence which contributes to excellent customer service. Systems and processes are designed around customers, whether internal or external.

Customer Loyalty

Some customers tend to return to the same service deliverer and this is customer loyalty. Obviously customer loyalty can be built up if the customer experience of an organisation has been good. Customer loyalty is valuable to an organisation because it is generally cheaper and easier to do repeat business with an existing satisfied customer than it is to find a new one. Some organisations choose to reward customer loyalty by making special customer service arrangements and offers for repeat customers. Generally customer loyalty means that if an organisation has a problem with a customer there is a better chance of keeping that customer afterwards than there would be with a new customer.

Customer Relationship Manager

A manager in an organisation who takes the lead in building and maintaining an ongoing relationship with a corporate customer.

Customer Satisfaction

Customer satisfaction is the feeling that a customer gets when he or she is happy with the customer service that has been provided. Some organisations try to increase customer satisfaction and talk about delighting customers or exceeding customer expectations. Most organisations try to increase the number of customers who are happy to confirm customer satisfaction when they give their customer feedback.

Customer Service

Customer service is the sum total of what an organisation does to meet customer expectations and produce customer satisfaction. Customer service generally involves service teamwork and service partnerships. Although somebody may take a leading part in delivering customer service it normally involves actions by a number of people in a team or in several different organisations.

Customer Service Framework

A strategically planned set of elements which will enable an organisation's customer service strategy to be successfully implemented. The framework typically includes (amongst other elements) an appropriate organisational structure, an operational plan and a plan for the development of customer service skills and knowledge amongst its employees.

Customer Service Process

Customer service processes are the routines and detailed steps an organisation uses to deliver its customer service. Some organisations have formal procedures in writing and use those to train staff and to monitor service. Many smaller organisations do not put their procedures in writing and the procedures are simply seen as 'the way we do things around here'.

Customer Service Strategy

A high level plan for the achievement of customer service excellence by a whole organisation. The strategy will typically include the timeframe and the methods of achieving service excellence.

Customer Centric Communication

Any method or channel of communication which focuses first and foremost on the needs of customers.

Customer Expectations
The set of services which an organisation's customer expects to receive.

Customer Experience
The experience of the individual customer in accessing the services of an organisation. This is critical, because it is often different from the perceptions of the organisation's employees and managers.

Customer Preferences
Each customer is an individual and customers tend to have different likes and dislikes. Sometimes, in order to deliver consistent customer service an organisation chooses to do things in exactly the same way for every customer. Sometimes it is possible to offer a customer options so that his or her customer preferences can be taken into account in the way the customer service is delivered.

Customer Relationship
A customer relationship forms as the result of a number of individual customer service transactions. Good customer relationships are important to a service provider because they build customer loyalty. This is valuable to an organisation because it is generally cheaper and easier to do repeat business with an existing satisfied customer than it is to find a new one.

Customer Transaction
A customer transaction, or customer service transaction, may be face to face or at a distance by telephone, in writing or by e-mail, and is a single exchange of information, product or service between a customer and a service deliverer. A series of customer service transactions build up a customer service relationship.

Deliver the Promise
Keep to what you and your organisation say you will do.

Diversity
The variation in individual needs and characteristics (which could include gender, ethnic background, skills and personality type for example) amongst customers and team members.

Easy to Do Business With
If the organisational competencies necessary for excellent customer service are in place, then customers will find the organisation easy to do business with.

E-Commerce
Business conducted primarily on the internet.

Ego State
One of three alternative ego states – either adult, child or parent - which people can adopt when interacting with others.

E-Learning
A form of learning which provides content, activates and assessments through an electronic medium such as the internet or a personal computer.

Emotional Intelligence
Emotional Intelligence is the ability to understand your own emotions and those of your customers, and how they can change in different situations.

Empathy
The caring, individualised attention that an organisation provides for its customers.

Environment
One element of a customer service strategy which considers factors external to the organisation, such as changes in the industry, changes in customers' expectations and new technologies.

Excellent Service
A level of service which means that your organisation is maximising its chances of being the market leader, constantly innovating to find new ways of exceeding customer expectations, with highly skilled and motivated individuals delivering exceptional service to customers. You are consistently attempting to exceed customers' expectations - every time a customer interaction takes place. This level of service really does consistently deliver the "Wow!" factor.

External Customer
An external customer is a customer from outside the organisation providing a product or service.

Financial Benefits
If the organisational competencies necessary for excellent customer service are in place, then an organisation can build its reputation for service excellence. This in turn leads to customer loyalty, recommendation, repeat and new business, and thereby financial success.

Focus Group
An interactive group discussion led by a facilitator. It tends to be relatively unstructured so that the facilitator can encourage the free flow of ideas.

Gap Analysis
A method of assessing the quality of customer service which measures the gaps between different peoples' perceptions of service - for example, the gap between employees' perceptions of how service is delivered and customers' perceptions of the service they actually receive. Unusually, several different service gaps are analysed so that an organisation can focus on closing the main gaps in order to improve service for customers.

Go the Extra Mile
Trying to exceed customers' expectations.

Handling Difficult Situations
The strategies and tools which may be used to resolve a range of problems and challenging customer service situations.

Hygiene Factor
In motivation theory, Herzberg (1968) claimed that employees are not generally motivated by the "carrot" (such as money or benefits), nor by the "stick" (such as being reprimanded for not achieving targets). However, hygiene factors, the necessary elements within an individual's working environment, such as company policies, management and working relationships, need to be present in order for the individual not to be de-motivated.

Informal Learning
A wide range of unstructured methods by which an individual can learn, including learning from others, from the media, websites, on-the-job activates and observing and conversing with colleagues.

Integrated Processes
Processes which work together or link together well, so that customers do not suffer from being transferred from one process or person to another.

Internal Customer
An internal customer is somebody from the same organisation as the service provider. They are treated as a customer so that they in turn can provide better customer service to external customers.

Job Enrichment
Providing extra interest, challenge and opportunity for development within an individual employee's job role.

Keep It Simple
Ensure that customers' experiences of doing business with an organisation are as straightforward as possible.

Make It Personal
Provide emotional content in service delivery, such as making a customer feel special or giving a customer individual attention.

Mission Statement
A mission statement is a brief statement of the main purpose or mission of the organisation. Many mission statements include commitments to customer service as a central purpose of the organisation in order to provide a focus for staff.

Moment of Truth

In any customer service procedure there are several points when customer awareness of the quality of customer service is particularly high. These points have a greater effect on customer perceptions of the customer service they have received. It is usually appropriate to pay particular attention to these moments of truth because they form customer opinions about customer service as a whole. 'Moments of truth' means the points in a transaction, service delivery or customer relationship at which customer expectations are at their sharpest and most demanding.

Motivating or De-Motivating Factors

The factors which can either increase or decrease an individual's commitment and enthusiasm for a task. These factors are highly specific to each individual.

Mystery Shopper

Acting as an anonymous customer in order to assess an organisation's service quality. A performance report is normally provided against predetermined criteria, so that the organisation can address any improvements that are needed.

Negative Delegation

Delegating repetitive and unchallenging tasks to a team member, not allowing the team member to develop their skills through the delegated tasks.

One-To-One

A face to face meeting, often between a manager and team member.

Operation

One of the components of a customer service strategy, the operation, or operational plan, usually involves detailed decision-making about resources, employees, processes and structures in the organisation which are needed in order to carry through the organisation's objectives.

Organisational Competencies

Applied to service, organisational competencies are the essential capabilities that the organisation as a whole should develop in order to achieve excellent and consistent service delivery for its customers.

Organisational Culture

All organisations have their own, distinct culture, often easily recognised by customers and employees. For excellent customer service, this culture needs to be closely focused on customers themselves.

Organisational Self Assessments

Measurements of the level of performance of different aspects of an organisation, often used in relation to the quality of customer service. Measurement is carried out by the organisation itself.

Organisational Values

Organisational values (or corporate values) are statements about the basic principles that an organisation and its employees intend to uphold. They may include standards for how customers will be treated.

Performance Objectives

Components of an organisation's customer service strategy which translate corporate objectives into specific targets, usually for each operational area of the organisation.

Performance Related Pay

Reward for employees based in part on the performance of the individual, team or organisation compared with predetermined objectives or targets.

Personal Qualities

A service characteristic important for service excellence which includes, for example, being trustworthy, proficient and professional.

Personal Touch

The provision of emotional content and/or individualised attention when interacting with customers.

Personal Vision Statement

An individual's written statement of their intentions within their personal life, career and professional development.

PESTLE Analysis

PESTLE stands for: Political, Economic, Sociological, Technological, Legal, Environmental. PESTLE analysis is used to conduct an audit of an organisation's environmental influences in order to help plan the strategic direction of the organisation.

Plan - Deliver - Follow-Up

A three-stage systematic approach to be followed when delivering service to customers.

Positive Delegation

Delegating challenging tasks to a team member, thus allowing the team member to develop their skills through the delegated tasks.

Problem Resolution

A generic term for solving a range of customer service breakdowns, challenges and difficulties.

Product Standards

Minimum or expected standards of delivery, applied to an organisation's products.

Professional Development Plan

A detailed plan for how an individual will develop their own professional capabilities, knowledge and skills. The plan is normally reviewed and updated on a regular basis.

Qualitative Research

The gathering of "soft" feedback (often from customers), which cannot easily be expressed in numerical terms. It could be obtained, for example, from finding out about the opinions of customers.

Quality Audit

Auditing or checking an organisation's performance of its planned processes, often conducted by sampling specific transactions and following their progress through the processes.

Quality Circle

A group composed of employees who meet to talk about workplace improvement, often making presentations to management with their ideas, especially relating to product and service quality, in order to improve the performance of the organisation, teams and individuals.

Quantitative Research

The gathering of "hard" feedback (often from customers), usually expressed in numerical terms or "facts and figures."

Questionnaire Fatigue

A problem experienced by customers if they are asked to complete too many survey forms. Customers can become tired and cynical about completing the questionnaires.

Regulator

Regulation that applies to a particular sector is generally enforced by a person or body appointed as regulator. Restrictions and rules created by the regulator may affect the way an organisation can deliver customer service.

Reliability

A service characteristic important for service excellence which includes, for example, always delivering good quality products and promptly delivering the items ordered by the customer.

Resolve Problems Well

The practice of resolving customers' difficulties and problems by responding effectively and swiftly with appropriate solutions.

Respond - Resolve - Improve

A three-stage systematic approach to be followed when resolving customer service problems. A key element in the routine is identifying problems' causes and thereby possible improvements.

Responsiveness

A service characteristic important for service excellence which includes, for example, being willing to help customers and provide a prompt resolution to problems.

Reward and Recognition

The sum total of monetary and non-monetary remuneration for a job done.

Risk Assessment

In order to look after the Health and Safety of customers it may be necessary to carry out a risk assessment. This involves identifying all the risks that may exist and assessing them for seriousness and for the likelihood of them happening. Health and Safety legislation requires service providers to carry out formal risk assessments in certain circumstances.

Seamless Service
The minimisation of the disruption caused by transferring customers between different people, departments or processes.

Security or Safety Needs
One of Maslow's hierarchy of needs which includes, for example, freedom from physical danger and having financial/job security.

Self-Actualisation Needs
One of Maslow's hierarchy of needs which includes, for example, maximising one's skills and talents, contributing to job satisfaction.

Self-Esteem Needs
One of Maslow's hierarchy of needs which includes, for example, being respected or looked up to others and having self-confidence.

Service Chain
The linking together of people and functions within an organisation and its supplier network in order to provide efficiency and seamless service for customers.

Service Characteristics
The critical set of competencies and behaviours that are important for service excellence.

Service Concept
This important part of an organisation's customer service strategy spells out the kind of service that the organisation wants to provide for its customers. It should be communicated and thereby help the whole organisation focus on what the organisation intends to achieve in relation to customer service.

Service Culture
An organisational competence which contributes to excellent customer service. There is a culture throughout the organisation's people that focuses on giving excellent service to both internal and external customers. Leaders and managers communicate the organisation's vision, values, leadership and continuous improvement methods to employees. Employees understand their own role in supporting the service culture.

Service Delivery Gap
Any gap between customers' expectation and the actual delivery of service to them.

Service Level Agreement
A statement, in specific and measurable terms, of the levels of service that an organisation will provide and that a customer can expect to receive.

Service Offer
A service offer defines the extent and limits of the customer service that an organisation is offering. In commercial organisations the service offer is partly or largely determined by the price that is being charged and by the service offer of competitors. A unique service offer is one that differentiates the offer that an organisation is making from that of its competitors or comparable organisations.

Service Partnership
A service partnership can be formed when two organisations or two departments of the same organisation combine in order to provide more effective customer service. Many organisations choose to use the service partnership model to encourage service teamwork and co-operation rather than identifying one party as the internal customer of the other.

Service Personality
An organisational competence which contributes to excellent customer service. The organisation has a well-defined personality which defines the particular way it delivers service and interacts with its customers.

Service Promise
The service promise is the sum total of service features/offers that a customer has been led to confidently expect from an organisation and its entire staff. It includes both what will be delivered and, more importantly, how it will be delivered. It is important that an organisation

describes this in a way that helps to clarify the promise for staff which will let them know what is expected and unite them in common activity.

Service Provider
A service provider is an organisation that provides customer service. Support staff play a vital part in the service teamwork with front line staff.

Service Recovery
Resolving problems effectively in customer service, and preferably correcting the cause of the problem to avoid recurrence.

Service Standards
Minimum or expected standards of delivery, applied to an organisation's services.

Shared Vision
A clear view of what an organisation intends to achieve, understood by all involved, including the organisation itself, its employees, its customers and its other stakeholders.

SMART Action Plan
SMART refers to Specific, Measurable, Achievable, Realistic and Time-constrained actions which make up an effective action list - helpful in making improvements and dealing with changes and problems

Social Needs
One of Maslow's hierarchy of needs which includes, for example, being accepted by one's colleagues.

Stereotyping
Taking a view about the characteristics, capabilities or behaviour of an individual based on a false view of the gender, nationality, culture or other category in which the individual can be placed.

Submissive Behaviour
A type of behaviour in which one gives in to other people, putting other peoples' feelings and wants before one's own.

Suggestion Scheme
An arrangement in a team or organisation which encourages individuals to identify innovations, improvements or simply good ideas. Some such schemes reward those making the suggestions.

Survival Needs
One of Maslow's hierarchy of needs which includes, for example, access to food, water, shelter, warmth, and sleep.

SWOT Analysis
A checklist approach to identifying and evaluating the Strengths, Weaknesses, Opportunities and Threats facing an organisation or team. It involves stating the organisation's or team's objective(s) and then identifying the internal and external factors that are helpful and unhelpful in achieving the objective(s).
Strengths: attributes of the organisation or team that are helpful to achieving the objective(s).
Weaknesses: attributes of the organisation or team that are harmful to achieving the objective(s).
Opportunities: external factors that are helpful to achieving the objective(s).
Threats: external factors which could damage to the performance of the organisation or team.

Tangibles
The physical facilities, equipment, personnel and communication materials provided by an organisation during the delivery of customer service.

Team Skills Audit
A systematic checking of the skills present within a team, often then matched against the specific set of skills required in order to deliver customer service.

Team Synergy
A benefit of team working in which the total capability of the whole team is enhanced by individuals working together effectively.

Time Management
The range of methods by which an individual prioritises and completes tasks in order to meet deadlines.

Touch-Point

A single interaction between a service deliverer and a customer. Such a touch-point can be critical in forming the customer's view of the organisation.

Transactional Analysis

Transactional Analysis (TA) is a framework for describing behaviour in an interchange between two people. It can help in understanding why people react the way they do, especially when dealing with difficult customer service situations. TA is one of the best known interpersonal skills models used to individuals' skills in handling interactions with other people. It originates from Eric Berne's book in the 1960's called "Games People Play."

Transactional Stimulus and Response

The transactional stimulus is the initial message sent by one of the participants in an interaction between two people. It could be one of the types: Adult, Child or Parent. This message or stimulus will normally be followed by a transactional response from the other person – which again could be either Adult, Child or Parent in type.

Understanding Customers

A service characteristic important for service excellence which includes, for example, taking the trouble to check on a customer's requirements and understanding the customer's business.

Vision Statement

A description of where an organisation aspires to be in the future. It may describe how the organisation sees itself over a period of perhaps 5 or 10 years if everything goes to plan.

Weblog

Often abbreviated to simply "blog," this is an internet web page or website which acts as a discussion medium, allowing the originator or owner of the blog (the "blogger") to start discussion topics to which others can respond.

Win-Win

The concept that both or all parties to a collaborative arrangement can benefit.

World Class Service Excellence

The highest level of customer service achieved by the very best customer service organisations globally.

Index

Notes